"You made a bad investment,"

Helen retorted. "Because nothing would ever induce me to have any kind of relationship with you!"

"You never asked me what sort of 'relationship' with you I had in mind, Helen. Doesn't it interest you at all?"

His smile was slow and dangerous.

"Marriage, Helen. How could I offer you anything less?"

Jennifer Taylor was born in Liverpool, England, and still lives in the northwest, several miles outside the city. Books have always been a passion of hers, so it seemed natural to choose a library career—a wise decision as the library was where she met her husband, Bill. Twenty years and two children later they are still happily married and she is still working in the library, with the added bonus that she has discovered how challenging and enjoyable writing romantic fiction can be!

Books by Jennifer Taylor

HARLEQUIN ROMANCE
3142—LOVESPELL

HARLEQUIN PRESENTS
1326—A MAGICAL TOUCH
1349—TENDER PURSUIT

LOVESTORM
Jennifer Taylor

Harlequin Books

TORONTO • NEW YORK • LONDON
AMSTERDAM • PARIS • SYDNEY • HAMBURG
STOCKHOLM • ATHENS • TOKYO • MILAN
MADRID • WARSAW • BUDAPEST • AUCKLAND

ISBN 0-373-17230-3

LOVESTORM

Copyright © 1994 by Jennifer Taylor.

First North American Publication 1995.

CHAPTER ONE

THERE were lights on all over the house. They spilled from the windows and chased away the shadows from the driveway, offering a welcome to all who were invited that night.

Jacob Hunt was entertaining, giving one of his renowned dinner parties. She could picture it now, the huge dining-room with its heavy oak furniture, the crystal and glass sparkling on the long table. The guests would be a mix of the rich and famous, the intellectual and witty, the very best that society could offer. That was why she had chosen tonight to come.

There was no hesitation as she rang the bell. She had made her plans carefully and knew what had to be done. Now it was a relief to get here and set them in motion.

'Good evening—Miss Helen!'

She felt an echo of the man's surprise but managed to hide it, forcing a smile as she walked through the open door. She hadn't known that Baxter was still here, but should have guessed. Jacob had wanted it all and now he had it, right down to the smallest detail.

'Good evening, Baxter. How are you?'

'Er—very well, thank you, Miss Helen.' The man glanced uncertainly over his shoulder then quickly recovered his composure. 'Mr Hunt is with guests at present. May I show you into the sitting-room while I inform him that you are here?'

'No, thank you, Baxter. That won't be necessary.' She brushed past him, her footsteps echoing as she crossed the hall and pushed the dining-room door open. They were all there, just as she'd imagined it. If she had set her mind to it she could have recognised most of the faces which turned towards her but she was interested only in one face, one man.

He was sitting at the head of the table, a glass of wine held in one lean hand. Under the glowing light from the chandeliers his hair shone a rich blue-black, his tanned skin gleamed. He was twenty-eight now but looked older. There was experience etched on that harshly carved face and lying in the depths of those deep blue eyes. Jacob Hunt had used every means in his power to get what he wanted and each had left its mark.

For a moment Helen almost hesitated as fear rose sharp and cold in her breast. She knew what he was capable of, knew what a bitter adversary he was, so had she been a fool to come? How could she hope to strike a blow against a man like him?

'Helen—what a charming surprise. Do join us.'

If he felt surprised at seeing her he didn't show it, that deep, smooth voice betraying just a hint of amusement. And that more than anything gave her the strength to carry on.

She closed the door and walked slowly along the length of the table until she stopped just a foot away from his chair. She could hear the murmurs from the guests, sense their curiosity, and had to hold back a bitter smile. No one seated around this table would ever forget this night!

'A surprise? Come now, Jacob, it can hardly be that. You knew that I would come, surely?'

Her voice was clear; it rang around the room and cut the conversation dead. She had everyone's attention now just as she had planned. These friends of Jacob's whom he had courted with money and deadly charm would soon find out what he was really like.

He lifted the glass to his lips and drank, watching her steadily over the rim in a way which made a tight little spiral of unease curl inside her. She looked away from those brilliant eyes then cursed herself for the slip when she heard the note in his voice. Jacob was too sharp to miss any sign of weakness. He was a hunter who stalked his prey, knew its weaknesses and vulnerabilities and used them to make the kill. She couldn't afford that sort of lapse again.

'Perhaps not, but I didn't expect to see you quite so soon.' He glanced at his watch then back at her with a faint lift of his brows. 'You must have come straight from the airport, I imagine.'

Helen didn't waste time in answering a question he knew the answer to, her face filled with contempt. 'You think you are so clever, don't you? You have it all now: the business, this house, even——'

'Even Richard?' He laughed out loud, the sound rumbling around the room. 'Come now, Helen, surely you aren't going to tell me that you are madly in love with him?' He shrugged lightly, the cloth of his elegant dinner-jacket straining across his shoulders. He had a superb body, lean and muscular, honed to perfection by years of hard work when he was younger. He still kept himself fit even though he didn't need to do anything more strenuous than issuing orders. It was just another thing which Helen hated about him.

'I don't intend to tell you anything, Jacob. How could I? You know all the answers, don't you? You decided what you wanted and made your plans and now you have it all—everything apart from the clothes on my back, and I believe that you are entitled to them as well.' She laughed softly, her face very pale against the gleaming red waves of hair which fell past her shoulders, her green eyes glittering almost feverishly. 'One thing no one can ever accuse me of, Jacob, is not paying my debts!'

She drew off her leather gloves and tossed them on to the table, then unbuttoned her black cashmere jacket and dropped it on to the floor at Jacob's feet, her eyes never leaving his. When her hands lifted to the tiny buttons down the front of her black silk dress she heard a woman gasp and felt a rush of elation. It would be all over town tomorrow, all these people he had courted so assiduously would be talking and speculating and Jacob would hate it!

'I think that's just about enough.' Jacob's voice cut through the silence although he had made no attempt to raise it. It was what Helen had anticipated, that Jacob would put a stop to what she was doing; what she hadn't expected was to hear that note of amusement in his deep voice.

Her fingers froze on the smooth cool silk, her eyes locked to Jacob as he stood up and smiled down the length of the table. 'Disappointed though you must all be, I am sure you will understand if I declare this dinner party over. Obviously Helen has gone to some lengths to claim my undivided attention so I feel that is what I must give her.' He slid a glance over Helen's rigid figure, his voice dropping to a level of intimacy which brought the colour rushing to her cheeks. 'I must confess that it won't be any hardship!'

There was a moment's stunned silence then several people laughed as they got to their feet. Helen barely heard the amused remarks or Jacob's smooth replies as she stared after the departing guests and felt suddenly afraid. This wasn't what was meant to happen. She had wanted them all to witness what she had planned, wanted to see Jacob humiliated in their eyes, but he had turned the tables on her. It was she who felt humiliated now!

With a murmur of distress she bent to pick up her jacket but Jacob was there before her, his grip bruising as his fingers closed around her wrists while he hauled her upright. 'Not leaving so soon, are you, Helen? Not when I have just gone to such lengths to ensure that we can talk without any interruptions?'

There was something in that deep voice which made her go cold and she struggled wildly to free herself but his hands just tightened, strong fingers bruising her white flesh.

'Let me go, Jacob! You have no right to manhandle me.'

'No?' He laughed softly, drawing her closer so that she could feel the hardness of his body against hers. 'You said yourself that I am entitled to the clothes off your back. I think that is an underestimation, Helen. I imagine that I am entitled to a lot more than that!'

'No!' With a surge of strength stemming from fear she pushed him away, but when she tried to run to the door he was there before her, barring her way. Slowly, with cool deliberation, he turned the key in the lock then slipped it into his jacket pocket as he walked back to the table and poured himself another glass of wine. He raised it aloft, his eyes glittering with mockery. 'A toast, Helen. At last I've managed to unleash some emotion from behind that ever-so-cool façade of yours.'

He drank the wine in one go then set the glass down, raising a mocking brow at her continued silence. 'Nothing to say, my dear? No response to my toast? The old Helen would have been far more gracious and remembered all those carefully instilled manners.'

'Damn you, Jacob Hunt! Damn you to hell and back for what you have done!'

He laughed aloud. 'I'm sure I was damned many years ago, so save your breath, my sweet.'

'I am not *your* anything! Do you hear me? I hate you, Jacob. I hate you for everything you have done to my family. You drove my father to bankruptcy, made certain that there was nothing left so that he was forced to sell you the business, the house, the land—everything! You wanted everything we had and did your damnedest to get it. And I despise you because of it!'

'And that is the reason why you came tonight, isn't it? Your hatred was great enough to break through the icy disdain you have treated me with all these years? I must admit to feeling a certain satisfaction that I understood you so well, Helen.'

'I have no idea what you're talking about. Please unlock the door. I want to leave.'

'So there is still a bit of the old Helen left. Even in a time of stress you can remember to say please. I imagine you will even thank me when I allow you to go, but not just yet. *Please* accept my invitation to stay a while longer. After all, Helen, you haven't really explained the reason for your visit, entertaining though it has been.'

His eyes dropped deliberately to the soft curves of her body under the clinging silk dress. Helen felt colour flood her face and turned away, but not fast enough to prevent Jacob from seeing it. When he laughed this time his voice held a note which made heat curl and shimmer inside her, awakening sensations she didn't want to feel.

'It's still there, isn't it, Helen? Oh, you've done your best over the years to pretend it doesn't exist but we both know differently. Does it offend you that you feel this awareness of me? Is that the reason why you keep your distance and try to convince yourself that you might possibly find happiness with Richard? Are you afraid of all those hot wild feelings? Afraid to touch the flame of real desire in case you get burnt?'

'No! Don't flatter yourself, Jacob Hunt. The only feelings I have for you are ones of contempt!' She tossed her head to send the gleaming rich red waves rippling down her back. 'It makes me laugh when I read about you in the paper, all those articles full of praise for all you've achieved in such a remarkably short time. You're seen as the perfect example of the self-made man who worked himself up from nothing to immense riches. How much are you worth now, Jacob? One million—ten? I doubt you have time to count your wealth because you're too busy acquiring more!'

'You make it sound like a crime, Helen.' He smiled faintly as he walked over to the window and stared out at the darkness of the night. Helen could imagine exactly what he was seeing, could picture in her mind's eye the long sweep of lawn down to the lake, the swaying movement of the trees in the distant wood. How many times had she stood exactly where Jacob was standing now, staring out at that same view? It was the memory of that which gave her the strength to carry on in the face of a growing fear.

'It is a crime! The way you set about achieving what you wanted was criminal.' She followed him across the room refusing to let him see her fear. 'You set out to destroy my family. You used any means you could to take everything we had away, and why? Because you were jealous. You resented us having things you didn't!'

'Is that the way you see it, Helen? Do you really imagine that my whole life has been one long war against your family?'

'Yes!' She spat the word back at him, glaring into his set face. 'You know it's true. From the minute you moved into the area when you were seventeen you hated us!'

'And is it any wonder?' His anger suddenly rose, his eyes burning with it as they met hers. 'You and your family and friends did all you could to humiliate me. You mocked my accent, my clothes, the home I lived in. I made a mistake, you see. I actually thought that I could become one of you, but that could never happen. I was too rough and poor to mix with the Sinclairs.' He caught her chin, his hold gentle, yet she knew she would have little hope of freeing herself without a struggle and she wouldn't give him that much satisfaction. 'But I found out in time what was going on, Helen, didn't I? Before I made an even bigger fool of myself and gave you and your friends more to laugh at?'

'I...' She couldn't think what to say, the words drying up under the force of that bitter stare. She closed her eyes, not wanting to recall that day by the lake so many years ago, but the memories were too vivid to blank them out.

They had all been there, Helen and all her friends, enjoying a day lazing by the lake under the hot July sun. All apart from Jacob. He had found himself a job working in one of the local garages and spent little time now hanging around on the edges of their circle. Helen couldn't remember which of the boys first started to mimic Jacob's rough city accent, but in no time at all the others had joined in, making increasingly derogatory comments about his clothes, the small rented cottage where he lived with his mother.

Helen had wanted to stop them but she'd been afraid to stand up for Jacob in case she'd found herself on the wrong end of the mockery. Jacob Hunt had disturbed her. He had aroused feelings inside her she'd barely understood and had no idea how to handle. Sometimes when he looked at her with those burning deep blue eyes she'd felt as though she were stepping in quicksand, and it had made her feel afraid and keep her distance from him.

When one of the girls had suddenly asked her if she didn't think Jacob was attractive, Helen had given a theatrical shudder of distaste, her voice cutting as she had stated that Jacob Hunt was too rough and too poor for her taste. Everyone had laughed, yet when Helen had looked round and suddenly seen Jacob standing in the shadow of the trees she had felt deeply ashamed. No one else had seen him. He had turned and left without a word, yet that day had lain between them all these years, never mentioned until just now yet at the root of everything that had happened since...

'It was just foolish talk, Jacob,' she said quietly now. 'Nobody would have said anything if they had realised you were there.'

He let her go so abruptly that she staggered back and had to steady herself against the wall. 'I'm sure they wouldn't have, Helen. They had far too much sense for that.' He smiled grimly and she looked away, understanding what he meant.

Jacob had been bigger than the rest of the boys his age, his body far more muscular. He had exuded a latent power which had kept the girls whispering about him for hours and made the boys both jealous and wary. If he had chosen to show his displeasure that day then no one would have been his match. But even then Jacob had been too clever for that. He had taken that hurtful conversation and used it to strengthen his determination to make them pay.

The resurgence of shame Helen had felt so briefly died as everything he had done came rushing back. She laughed bitterly, her face mirroring her contempt and hatred almost in equal measures.

'But in the end you had the last laugh, didn't you? I mean, look at you now.' Her eyes skimmed his powerful body then came to rest on his face. 'Rich, influential— you have everything you want, everything you ever dreamed of having.'

He shook his head, his eyes hooded as he unfastened the elegant black bow tie and tossed it on to the table then flicked open the top buttons of his dress shirt. His skin was just as tanned at the base of his strong throat as it was on his face. He'd come back from a holiday at his private house in Nassau only a week ago and the colour of his skin spoke volumes of the hours he must have spent water-skiing and swimming.

Now, as Helen glimpsed the tantalising sight of that smooth, tanned skin, she felt her insides tighten in a way she hated. Deliberately she walked over to the table and poured herself a glass of the excellent wine. It was one she recognised, one from the fine cellar her father had built up over the years. Jacob owned all that now, every bottle, just as he owned every stick of furniture in this house where she had grown up. If she lived to be a hundred she would never forgive him for what he had done!

'Aren't you curious, Helen?'

His voice drew her back to the present and she took a sip of the wine she didn't want before putting the glass carefully down on the table and arching a slender brow at him. 'Curious? Sorry, Jacob, but I seem to have missed something.' She feigned a yawn, glancing at the tiny jewelled watch on her wrist, the only item she'd managed to save from the sale of her jewellery. Her father had given it to her for her twenty-first birthday and she would never part with it if she could help it. It was a reminder of all she'd had and lost, a reminder of why she should hate the man standing across the room.

He ignored her attempt at indifference, his face betraying little as he studied her. 'You said that I have everything I ever wanted but you were wrong, Helen. There is one thing I still want.'

What was it in his voice that made her feel suddenly uneasy? She searched his dark face but there was nothing there to explain why that shiver of unease should slide so devastatingly down her spine. She gave a small shrug of indifference as she picked up the glass again and raised it to her lips. 'Is there? How fascinating.'

He laughed then, softly, as though he understood completely how she felt and perhaps he did. Jacob had always been perceptive. He wouldn't have achieved what he had if he hadn't been. 'Aren't you going to ask me what it is? Surely your curiosity is piqued, Helen, by such a confession?'

She sighed deeply. 'If it means that we can end this whole charade then I suppose I shall have to. So, Jacob, what is the one thing you still want to complete your life?'

'You.'

The single word seemed to fill the silence, growing bigger and bigger with each second until she could feel it beating against her, inside her, drumming and throbbing like something live. As though from a great distance she saw the glass drop from her hand, watched the wine spread like blood across the damask tablecloth, heard the shattering tinkle of breaking glass, yet she couldn't seem to move.

She had come tonight to hurt him, to make him pay for everything he had done, but she had been a fool to imagine she could achieve that. Jacob Hunt was invulnerable. He had proved that time and again as he had ruthlessly clawed his way to the top. He was a predator without mercy and she had just made the biggest mistake of her life to forget that.

She had entered the lion's den meaning to wound him and by doing so allowed herself to get trapped!

CHAPTER TWO

THERE was a soft tapping on the door. Helen heard it only vaguely. Her head was reeling, her whole body consumed by shock. When Jacob crossed the room to answer it she stared almost blankly at Baxter, who stood uncertainly in the doorway.

'Is everything all right, Mr Hunt?'

'Fine, think you, Baxter. Miss Sinclair just had a slight accident and broke a glass. See that it is cleared up immediately, please.' Jacob glanced back over his shoulder, his eyes narrowing as they fell on Helen's still figure. 'And bring the first-aid box to the study. Miss Sinclair appears to have cut her hand.'

Helen glanced down at her hand, only then becoming aware of the long gash on her finger. She hadn't noticed it before and now she could feel it starting to throb as blood oozed from the cut. She picked up her bag to find a handkerchief to wrap around it, but suddenly Jacob was there beside her, his fingers firm as he lifted the bag from her hands.

'Leave it. I'll put a dressing on it when I have the first-aid box. Come into the study, then Baxter can get this mess cleared up.'

He slid his hand under her elbow but Helen pulled away from his hold at once. 'I'm not going anywhere with you. I want to leave.'

He smiled thinly, his blue eyes lingering on the stark pallor of her face, the line of white circling her lips. 'I

17

don't think you are in a fit state to go anywhere just yet, Helen. I have no intention of allowing you to go rushing off to have an accident.'

'You won't allow it? Damn you, Jacob, just who do you think you are to issue your orders? You don't own me!'

'No?' His face filled with mockery, his eyes glittering coldly into hers. 'I thought that was why you had come tonight, Helen? Because you had suddenly found out that I *do* own you. I own everything you have from the flat you live in to the clothes on your back.' His gaze dropped to the black silk dress and the curves of her body beneath. 'You have been the most beautiful investment I've ever made and now I hope to reap some rewards from it.'

'Damn you, Jacob! You are totally despicable! You forced my father into a corner so that he couldn't refuse your offers to help!' She tossed the heavy, silky weight of her hair back, glaring up at him with pure hatred in her eyes.

'Is that what he told you? Is that how he explained why he was so eager to accept the offer of a place to live rent-free, enough money to meet his bills?' His laughter was harsh and cutting. It made Helen take a step back but Jacob caught her arm and forced her to meet his angry gaze. 'Your father almost snapped my hand off when I told him what I was prepared to do. Perhaps you should take a leaf out of his book, Helen, and forget your pride. It is a luxury I doubt you can afford now.'

She wasn't aware of raising her hand. It was only when she heard the sickening sound of it striking his lean cheek that she realised what she had done. For one long moment Helen stared at her handiwork then turned and fled along the hall, but she wasn't fast enough to evade him.

When Jacob caught her around the waist and half dragged, half lifted her towards the study, she struggled wildly, her hand raising once more.

'Don't!' His voice was black ice as he uttered the single word, his eyes glittering with an anger that made her shrink away from him. When he hustled her into the room then closed the door as he let her go, she backed away from him at once and saw him smile in a way which sent a shiver down her spine.

'That's right, Helen. Opt for caution this time. Don't ever forget that I am not one of your milk-and-water men-friends.'

'I loathe you, Jacob Hunt,' she hissed out from between tight-drawn lips. 'I hate you more than ever now that I've found out what you have been up to!'

'If your father had been any sort of a man then you would have found out about it sooner, sweetheart. In fact, if he had been any sort of a man at all he would never have accepted my offer in the first place.'

'And why did you make it?' She laughed bitterly. 'I know how you feel about me and my family so I can't believe it was the result of some sudden rush of conscience! There had to be something else behind it all.'

'There was. Haven't you worked that out yet, Helen? Come, come. It's not like you to be so slow.' He walked over to the drinks table and poured himself some brandy, then stood warming it between his hands as he watched her.

'I'm afraid I find it difficult to understand how a mind like yours works, Jacob.' She shrugged dismissively but it was merely an attempt to hide her fear. She'd been shocked and horrified when her father had told her the truth last night. She'd spent hours going over it all, trying to understand why Jacob had done such a thing, but even now she couldn't fully understand his motives. Bit by bit he had whittled away at the very fabric of her life, taking the business, the house, even Richard.

She had been stunned when Richard had told her a few weeks ago that he had accepted an offer from Hunt Electronics and would be flying out to New York for training before taking on a management post with the company. He knew nothing about the long-running feud with Jacob so had seen nothing strange about the wonderful opportunity. Helen had known differently at once. Jacob had offered Richard the position because of her. She and Richard had been seeing each other for almost a year, but although recently Richard had started talking tentatively about marriage Helen had hesitated about making such a commitment. Richard was pleasant company and she was fond of him, but marriage was a step she didn't feel ready for.

However, when Richard had told her with more than a touch of pride that he had been head-hunted by the prestigious firm, Helen hadn't had the heart to tell him her suspicions. Jacob Hunt was deliberately removing Richard from her life to ruin her chances of happiness. Then when she had discovered those cheques signed by Jacob in the desk drawer last night and her father had finally told her the truth, it had been the final straw. But anger had clouded her reasoning and that was a dangerous mistake to make around Jacob!

'Why do I get the feeling that wasn't a compliment?'

'Probably because you know it would be a cold day in hell before I ever paid you a compliment! Let's cut out the verbal fencing, Jacob. It isn't like you to be so reticent about your aims.'

'All right then, Helen. If you want the plain unvarnished truth then you can have it. Everything I have done has had but one purpose and that was to get you. I told you earlier that you were the one thing I still want, so it can't come as a total surprise.'

'And do you really imagine that I feel beholden to you for paying our bills and giving us somewhere to live?' She laughed out loud then bit her lip when she heard it starting to get out of control. 'I suppose you must have done, but I'm afraid you've wasted your money. You made a bad investment, Jacob, because nothing would ever induce me to have any kind of relationship with you!'

'Not even if I threaten to have you and your father evicted immediately?' He shrugged as he watched her face. 'You live there rent-free so I would be within my rights.'

He had thought of everything, of course. Right down to the finest detail. It just served to prove exactly what he was like. Helen smiled with chilling sweetness, her face filled with contempt. 'I would tell you to go straight ahead. If you throw us out then we shall find somewhere else to go, but just think of all the bad publicity it could create for you, Jacob. Imagine what the papers would make of your actions if I told, or rather sold, my story to them.' She laughed with faint triumph. 'I'm sure I would need the money, wouldn't I? Because your next threat just has to be to stop paying our living expenses. Am I right?'

He smiled slowly, his teeth gleaming against his tanned skin, his blue eyes crinkling at the corners. He raised the brandy glass and drank, then set it down calmly on the desk. 'I wonder if I have underestimated you, sweet Helen? You seem to have a counter-move for everything I do.'

Elation was so sweet she felt drunk on it. She smoothed the black silk dress over her hips then re-fastened the top button. 'You win some, you lose some, Jacob. You must know that?'

'I do. What is that saying about even the best laid schemes....?' He gave a faint, dismissive shrug of his wide shoulders, his eyes never leaving her face. Helen shifted uncomfortably, something about the situation making her uneasy. It wasn't like Jacob to give in so easily, yet what could he do now that she had made it plain she wouldn't be blackmailed into anything? It was laughable really; he had truly believed that she would meekly fall in with his plans just to keep a roof over her head and a few pounds in the bank! It was like something out of a story, the dutiful daughter sacrificing herself for the good of her family. Well, it was going to be tough, but somehow she and her father would manage!

She turned to leave the room and put an end to the whole ridiculous situation, then slowed to a halt when Jacob spoke. 'You never asked me what sort of a "relationship" with you I had in mind, Helen. Doesn't it interest you at all?'

The feeling of unease was growing stronger. It slid coldly down her spine, made her legs feel weak and shaky. It was an effort to turn back to look at him but she made herself do it, afraid to let him see her fear.

'Not much, but I suppose good manners dictate that I at least make some pretence of interest. So, Jacob, what did you have in mind?'

His smile was slow and dangerous, so sensual as it travelled the length of her body that Helen could feel it. Heat shimmered along each vein, following the slow stroke of those incredibly blue eyes so that she felt breathless when they finally stopped on her face.

'Marriage, Helen. How could I offer you anything less?'

She couldn't seem to find anything to say. The words seemed to be lost somewhere in the depths of her mind as she stared into his face and saw the truth.

'I—no!' She drew in a sharp breath but it didn't help to ease the tightness in her chest. 'I would never marry you in a million years, Jacob Hunt. No matter what kind of threats you made!'

He laughed softly. 'Then why are you getting so upset, Helen? You have just told me in no uncertain terms that you won't be coerced or blackmailed, so what are you so afraid of?' He leaned back in the chair, studying her calmly. 'The prospect of being out on the street and penniless doesn't bother you. You are prepared to suffer for your principles and even allow your father to suffer also.' He steepled his fingers, watching her over the top of them.

'Don't forget that I am quite prepared to go to the papers, Jacob.'

'Mmm, very brave of you. I'm sure I wouldn't do such a thing in your position.'

'What do you mean, "my position"? I am not the one making threats!'

'Oh, yes, you are, Helen. You are threatening to expose
me as some sort of ruthless, uncaring monster, yet look
at the facts, my sweet. I have allowed you and your father
to occupy that flat all these weeks without paying a
penny's rent *and* I've paid all your living expenses into
the bargain.' He shrugged. 'It was only ever meant to
be a temporary arrangement, of course. I'm sure your
father must have told you that. After all, he did sign an
undertaking to that effect.'

'What undertaking?' She was shaking now, tiny ripples
spreading through her whole body. She had a feeling
that everything was slipping out of her control to move
in a direction Jacob had planned for it, but that was
ridiculous. He was in the wrong, not her!

'Oh, just a small formality. I've always had it in mind
to use that flat myself—it's in such a prime position,
isn't it, Helen? Naturally, I felt it wise to safeguard my
options so had your father sign to say that he would
vacate the flat at the end of three months. There's just
over a week to go before our contract ends. But I'm sure
the papers you contact will bear that in mind when I put
the facts to them. Actually, going to them could be ben-
eficial to me. There can't be many people who would
take such a philanthropic stance, can there, Helen?'

'There is a word to describe you, Jacob, but it isn't
that one! You are a bast——!'

He cut her off, his face hard although his voice betrayed little of his emotions. 'Save your breath, Helen.
I've had that description hurled at me more times than
I can count over the years and in every shade of its
meaning.'

She flushed, suddenly deeply ashamed. Rumours had
been rife in the village when Jacob and his mother moved

in to the small rented cottage. The story was that Mrs Hunt was a widow, but few had believed it. Jacob had never spoken about his father and cut dead any attempts to question him. She didn't doubt that he had suffered because of it.

He must have seen her discomfort because he laughed. 'So maybe there is hope after all, Helen?' When she frowned he continued softly, his voice very deep in the silence. 'It upsets you to realise you might have scored too deep a blow?'

She drew herself up, staring back at him, not wanting him to think he had discovered any hint of weakness. Jacob was too cunning an adversary not to act upon it. 'Don't kid yourself, Jacob. I don't give a damn about your feelings!'

'Then you have a strange way of showing it. Still, never mind that now. I'm sure we shall have many future opportunities to discuss that.'

'There won't be *any* future opportunities. Your plan won't work, Jacob, because I don't care what you threaten me with. Now, if you will excuse me, I think I would prefer to leave. The air in here is starting to get foul.'

She left without another word, brushing past a startled Baxter who was just crossing the hall with the first-aid box in his hands. All she wanted was to get out of the house and away from this whole ridiculous situation. That Jacob should actually believe that he had put her in a position whereby she would be forced to marry him was incredible!

It was only later, alone in her room that night, that the fear started to grow. Whatever Jacob Hunt had set out to achieve, he had achieved it. And now it appeared he had set his sights on her!

'So you will try to be here, Father, won't you? The man from the removal firm said that he'll call at eleven to look around and give us an estimate.' Helen sighed as she looked round the elegant room. 'Not that it will take him long. Most of the furniture belongs here, so we shall have to try to find somewhere furnished to move to as we can't afford to buy much. What do you think?'

'It's up to you, Helen. I shall leave you to make the decisions.' Edward Sinclair got up slowly. 'I think I'll just go out for my paper now, dear.'

Helen watched him go, her heart aching. He seemed to have aged ten years since she'd arrived back that night almost a week ago and told him she had been to see Jacob. He had listened without uttering a word as she had explained that there was no way they could remain in the flat, although she hadn't explained what had gone on. She had no intention of discussing what Jacob had told her with anyone, not even her father!

Now, as she heard the front door close behind him, she sank down on a chair. There was so much to do, so many obstacles to overcome, from finding somewhere to live to finding some sort of a job to support them both. She'd been scouring the papers for weeks now but the plain fact was she had no experience. When her mother had been taken ill she had devoted herself to looking after her and her father and running the house rather than to a career. Now she wished she hadn't been so shortsighted. The trouble was that the Sinclairs had always had money. It had come as a shock to learn that they had lost it all after Jacob had driven the business into bankruptcy.

She had believed her father when he had told her that they'd been lent the flat by an old friend and that there was just enough money left to pay their bills. He had been trying to protect her from the truth, of course, but Helen wished he hadn't. Allowing Jacob to subsidise them had been a grave mistake!

Her mouth thinned at the thought of Jacob Hunt, and she got up to walk briskly into her bedroom to collect her coat. They would manage somehow. She wouldn't accept another penny of that man's money! She had an interview at a temping agency that morning so maybe this could be the break she needed.

When the doorbell rang Helen was in the hall. Thinking that it was her father coming back without his key, she opened the doors then turned her attention back to buttoning her elegant navy wool coat, tucking a jade-green silk scarf into the neckline to ward off the morning chill. It was September and the mornings were cool enough now to demand a coat.

'I won't be long, Father. Now don't forget about the removal firm, will you? Otherwise——'

'Otherwise you will have to rely on my hospitality a while longer, Helen?'

Jacob closed the door behind him as he stepped into the hall, his mouth curled in a lazy smile as he saw the shock which crossed her face at his unexpected appearance.

She collected herself almost immediately, her green eyes blazing at him. 'What do you want?'

He raised a dark, quizzical brow, his tone silky with menace as he walked past her into the huge sitting-room.

'What do you think I want, my sweet? Naturally I am interested to see that my property is being cared for.'

There was a faint emphasis on the word 'property' and despite herself Helen felt the colour start to her cheeks. Abruptly, she turned away and picked up the telephone, punching buttons with a shaking finger. 'I'm ringing the police, Jacob. I intend to tell them that a man has just forced himself inside my home so I suggest you leave before they arrive!'

'Your home?' He sat down on the sofa, watching her with amusement through the open doorway. 'Haven't you forgotten something? This is my property, Helen. I am entitled to enter and leave as I choose.'

Her fingers hesitated on the display of numbers before she slowly replaced the receiver on its rest. 'Don't worry, Jacob, you will soon be in full possession of your property. Father and I will be leaving just as soon as I can find us somewhere else to go.'

He shook his head. 'I doubt I can wait that long, Helen. Business dictates that I stay in town far more often than I have been doing up till now, so I shall expect you to vacate the flat by the end of the week.'

'The end of...' She broke off, taking a deep steadying breath, but it did little to ease the panic she could feel inside her. 'You know that's impossible, Jacob.'

He ran his hand through his black hair, smoothing it back from his forehead in a casual gesture which spoke of indifference. 'Is it? I'm sorry, but I'm afraid in the circumstances my generosity must be curtailed. I am a businessman, Helen. I expect a return on my investments. If I can see no hope of getting one then naturally I draw out of any deal and save my money for some other more profitable venture.'

Her eyes gleamed with contempt as she walked slowly into the room and stared at him. 'Meaning, I don't doubt, that as I have no intention of becoming your *wife* you don't see any reason to continue with your philanthropy?'

His mouth thinned at the note in her voice but he gave no other sign of displeasure. 'Something like that. It seems a pity that you are being so shortsighted about all this, Helen. If it had been just you who would suffer then maybe I could understand it, but the fact that you are prepared to stand aside and see people you love suffer too...' He shrugged, standing up to walk towards the door. He was dressed in a dark grey suit with a pale grey shirt and silk tie, clothes which bore all the hallmarks of civilisation, but there was little one could call really civilised about Jacob. He followed no rules of combat to fight for what he wanted, and even knowing that couldn't stop Helen from responding to that deliberately provocative statement.

'If you mean Father, then don't worry, Jacob, I shall take care of him.'

He stopped beside her, so close that she could see the tiny white lines fanned out from the corners of his eyes, smell the faint clean aroma of soap which clung to his skin. Her senses stirred at once, that hot, swift and totally inexplicable surge of awareness she always felt whenever he was near running unhindered through her body, and she looked away, terrified that he would see it.

'I'm sure you will do all you can, Helen. You are a resourceful woman, as I have come to appreciate. However, I do wonder if you will need far more resourcefulness than you realise. There's that operation your father needs, for instance.' He reached out and turned her face back to his, letting her go as soon as her shocked eyes met his and held.

'What operation? I don't know what you're talking about!'

'Don't you? Your father probably didn't want to worry you with it all, but you must have noticed the difficulty he's having walking now?' He paused while he studied her, his blue eyes betraying nothing but a faint concern which was so false that Helen felt her temper rise.

'I don't need you to tell me anything about my father!'

'No? Perhaps not. However, one thing you don't know is that I was prepared to pay for him to have the operation done privately. Waiting lists for the National Health are so long, but if you are prepared to let him deteriorate then that's your decision.'

'How dare you! Get out, Jacob—now! I won't listen to your horrible lies and insinuations a moment longer.' She started towards the door but he stopped her with a hand on her arm, his face hard now.

'It's time you did listen, Helen. Time you listened and understood everything you are doing. *You*, not me.' He gave her a small shake, his fingers biting into her flesh. She'd had bruises from the last time he had held her so roughly and she didn't doubt she would have more now. But ever since they had met, Jacob had inflicted bruises of one kind or another on her.

'I am not doing anything at all! So don't try to cover up your own unspeakable deeds. If father needs an operation then he shall have it. He has health insurance which he has paid for years.'

'Does he?' He smiled slowly, his fingers gentling against her skin so that they seemed to caress rather than restrain. 'I would check that out just to be certain, sweet.

You might find that along with the house, the business and everything else which was a part of your former lifestyle, that too is now just a pleasant memory.' He paused to let the full import of that sink in, but not too long, hitting her with a new fresh blow before she could recover. That was the kind of tactic Jacob employed, hitting the enemy blow after blow to bring him to his knees.

'And of course there is Richard. Surely you haven't forgotten your poor besotted admirer, Helen?'

She went cold, her blood freezing as she heard the note in that smooth, deliberate voice. Somewhere along the way Jacob had shed his former accent but just occasionally as now there was a trace of it to be heard. Helen found it strangely disturbing. It took her back in time to that moment when she had looked round and seen Jacob by the tree listening to the cruel, mocking comments being made about him. There had been something wild and dangerous on his face then, something which spoke of retribution. Now Helen sensed it once again.

Her voice was thin, reedy as she finally spoke. 'What have you done to Richard? Tell me, Jacob, damn you!'

'Nothing—yet. However, I really do not see that he can continue in his present position, Helen. Definitely not. Not when he has such strong links to you.'

'You mean you intend to sack him?' She tossed her hair back, staring into his blue eyes as she searched for an answer and found it immediately. She dragged her arm free of his hold and walked over to the window, feeling the urge to cry against her own impotence.

'I'm sure I don't need to answer that question, do I, Helen? You must see what an invidious position you have put me in. It's a pity about Richard, because he does show promise and I imagine he will find it almost impossible to find something else. Stepping up is a simple enough process but to find a job, and an employer willing enough to offer it, when it is an obvious step down is a wholly different matter.' He gave a faint sigh. 'Still, that's the way it goes.'

'I hate you, Jacob.' Her voice was no more than a thread as it carried across the room. She turned to face him, her skin very pale, the light from the window setting fire to her hair so that it glowed around her head. 'I hate, loathe and detest everything about you.'

'Do you, Helen? Oh, I don't doubt that you *think* you hate me but somehow I'm not completely convinced that's all you feel.' His eyes seemed to bore right through her and she drew in a tiny shocked breath, feeling more afraid than she'd ever felt before.

'It is, Jacob. The only thing I feel for you is hatred. Understand?'

He smiled faintly, his eyes holding hers for a moment longer before he glanced at his watch. 'Interesting though it would be to continue this discussion, I am afraid I shall have to leave. You know where to find me, Helen, if you suddenly come to your senses and realise what a mistake you're making.'

He left without another word and Helen turned back to stare out of the window with blank, unseeing eyes. Jacob was wrong! All she felt for him was hatred nothing more. She—hated—Jacob Hunt! Yet even as she chanted the words silently she could hear the thread of desperation woven through them, and it made her feel afraid.

CHAPTER THREE

IT had been raining all day, and by the time Helen arrived home in the early afternoon she was wet through and miserable. It had been a long and frustrating week, the search for a job and somewhere suitable to live proving fruitless. That there had been a security scare on the Underground, which had closed several lines so that she'd had to walk home, had seemed like the perfect ending to it. But as she walked into the foyer of the flats and found her father sitting in a chair by the reception desk, she knew it wasn't over yet.

'Father? What's happened? What are you doing here? I thought you would be at your club as usual?' Helen stopped beside the elderly man, viewing him with concern. Edward Sinclair had never been robust but he seemed to be growing more fragile by the day. Now, as he turned to her with relief, Helen could see his thin hands trembling around the stick he was forced to use all the time now to walk with.

'I came home early. It was far too noisy. Some young fellows... Then when I got here I—I didn't know what to do. Thank goodness you're here!'

Helen crouched down beside his chair and covered his hands with hers, hating to see the distress on his lined face. 'Don't worry, darling. Just tell me what's happened and I'll sort it out.'

'It's the flat, you see. I can't get in.'

Helen smiled in sudden relief, feeling her fear fading. 'So that's it. You've forgotten your key again. Never mind, it's easily done.' She stood up then frowned as she glanced across at the porter behind the desk. 'But why on earth didn't you ask Arthur to let you in? He has a key.'

The man behind the desk looked up, more than a trace of embarrassment on his face. 'I'm afraid I couldn't do that, Miss Sinclair.'

'Couldn't? What on earth do you mean?' She moved a step closer to the man, feeling her heart suddenly starting to pound as some sixth sense warned her there was more to that simple statement than appeared.

The porter shifted uncomfortably, looking down at the paper he held in his hands to avoid meeting her eyes. 'Mr Hunt had the locks changed on the flat this morning after you and your father left. He said—he said that in no circumstances was I to let anyone into the flat.'

Helen stared at him in open-mouthed horror for one long second, then felt a surge of red-hot anger rise inside her. She should have known! She should have guessed that Jacob would do something like this. All week long she'd tried to put the memory of his visit to the flat out of her mind, but she'd been a fool to imagine that refusing to think about Jacob would make him magically disappear!

'What are we going to do, Helen? Where shall we go?' Edward Sinclair's voice shook as he asked the questions and Helen fought to recover her control rather than upset him further. She forced a smile to lips which felt cold and stiff, patting his thin arm. 'Don't worry, father. This is all some sort of misunderstanding. Jacob—well, Jacob mentioned something about having the locks renewed when he popped in the other day. He probably doesn't realise that he has locked us out.'

'Oh, I see. Of course you're right, darling. Jacob has been more than generous these past months. He wouldn't have done this deliberately, I'm sure.' He must have seen Helen's involuntary start because he smiled sadly. 'Oh, I know you and Jacob don't see eye to eye, Helen, but there is an awful lot you don't know. I am sure you would change your views dramatically if you were in full possession of the facts.'

She doubted it! From where she was standing all the facts looked completely cut and dried. However, there was no way she wanted to add to her father's distress by arguing about it. Somehow she had to sort out this mess and the only way to do that was by going to see Jacob. It wasn't a thought she relished.

It was almost an hour later when she arrived at the towering glass and steel building which housed the head-quarters of Hunt Electronics. Helen paused on the pavement outside, staring up. She'd never been here before but she'd read about it. Over the past few years the papers had carried many stories about the success Jacob Hunt had made of his business ventures. He had moved into this showpiece office block last year, taking over five whole floors. It was just one more measure of how far up the ladder he had climbed.

The lift was smooth and silent as it whisked her up to the fifteenth floor. Helen barely had time to collect herself before the doors were gliding open. She stepped out on to pale grey carpet and into a setting of under-stated luxury. From the delicate mauve-tinted walls with their expensive Impressionist prints to the heavy, elegant black furniture, the whole place spoke of the money that had been spent. It just made Helen's temper inch another notch higher.

Jacob's office was at the end of a long corridor. Helen knocked on the outer office door then walked straight over to the elegant brunette seated behind the desk.

'I wish to see Mr Hunt.'

'Mr Hunt is extremely busy. I am afraid he has appointments for the rest of the afternoon.' The woman's smile was professionally polite but it held little warmth as it rested on Helen's face. But there was no way she was going to be deterred.

'I am quite sure that he will find time to see me. Would you please inform him that I am here. My name is Sinclair, Helen Sinclair.'

'Helen! What on earth are you doing here?'

Helen swung round at the sound of the familiar voice, stunned to see Richard crossing the room towards her. Dutifully she returned the kiss he bestowed on her cheek, then drew back, her face mirroring her confusion. 'I might well ask the same of you. I didn't know that you were due back in England yet, Richard. You made no mention of it in your letters.'

Richard grimaced, drawing Helen away from the secretary's desk to lead her back to the arrangement of chairs by the window. 'So you did get them? I was starting to wonder when I received no reply.'

Helen avoided his eyes, not wanting to confess that writing to Richard had been low down her list of priorities. 'I've been very busy. I'm sorry, Richard. But you haven't answered my question. What are you doing here?'

'I wish I knew! I've been here a while now, but frankly I've no idea what Hunt wants with me.' He gave a faintly nervous smile, his gaze moving to the closed door of Jacob's office. He was a good-looking man with fair hair, a few years older than Helen. She had always found him to be kind and reliable if rather unexciting company, but then excitement hadn't been what she'd been looking for. However, she had never seen him exhibit such nervousness before and it made her feel uneasy, although she couldn't explain why.

She drew her hands from his and sat down, motioning Richard to join her. 'Did Jacob send for you?'

Richard nodded, shooting another glance at the closed door. 'Yes. I've no idea what's going on, Helen, but I have this feeling that something awful is about to happen.'

Helen looked away from his worried face, feeling her own unease growing. Richard was right to worry; there was something going on, something Jacob had warned her would happen. Jacob had given Richard this job because of her and he would take it from him for the same reason.

'Miss Sinclair—Mr Hunt says that he will see you now.'

The secretary's voice held a note of surprise which Helen didn't share. Jacob had known she would come. It had been part of his plan, another move towards getting what he wanted. It was that quicksand effect again, each step she took drawing her in deeper and deeper until she couldn't get out. But if Jacob thought he would get away with it he was mistaken!

There was fire in her eyes as she entered the office, only to come to a sudden halt when she found it empty. She looked around, then walked over to a door standing partly open on the other side of the room, glanced through it and froze at the sight which met her eyes.

Jacob was lying on a black leather bench, his arms straining as he raised the bar of weights above his head. Apart from a pair of black shorts he was naked, his bronzed torso gleaming with perspiration. He looked round as he heard Helen's footsteps and soft gasp of surprise, then slowly let the weights slide back into place on their rest and slid off the bench. He stood up and took a towel from a rack, wiping his face with it before draping it carelessly around his neck. 'Annette said that you wished to see me.'

Helen's mouth felt strangely dry, her blood heavy and slow. She looked away from him, hating the way just the sight of him like this could disturb her so, and heard him laugh softly.

'Sorry, Helen. Does seeing me like this offend you? I would have waited until I had showered and changed if I had stopped to consider your delicate sensibilities, but I do have other appointments.' He paused deliberately, his voice smooth as silk when he continued, 'I imagine you saw Richard waiting outside?'

Her temper spiralled, wiping away that momentary weakness. 'You knew I would see him. It was all part of your rotten, horrible plan, wasn't it, Jacob? You knew I would come here, didn't you? That's why you arranged his appointment for today.'

He shrugged carelessly, dragging the towel from his neck to rub it over his chest and arms. 'You flatter me, Helen. You make it sound as though I'm omnipotent and I am hardly that. I couldn't have known exactly when you would arrive.'

She laughed harshly. 'Perhaps not, but it was simple enough to keep Richard waiting until I turned up!' She shot a venomous look around the small room with its array of exercise equipment, then let her eyes return to Jacob's face. 'You could easily delay seeing Richard while you dealt with all these other "appointments".'

He smiled slowly, walking past her towards a glass-enclosed shower stall fitted into one corner of the room. 'You have a suspicious mind, my sweet. Now, if you'll excuse me, I need to take a shower before we get down to the reason for this visit of yours.'

Helen caught his arm, her fingers closing around the hard muscles. His skin felt warm and smooth, faintly damp from his exertions, and she let him go at once. 'You know why I came, Jacob. It doesn't need any discussion. You changed the locks on the flat.'

'Yes. I did warn you that I wanted you out by the end of the week, Helen. It's hardly my fault if you chose to ignore that warning.'

'It wasn't a case of me ignoring it! Damn it, Jacob, do you imagine that I want to stay there any longer than I have to? It just isn't that easy to find somewhere else in so short a time!'

'That is hardly my concern, is it? You made your choice the other day, Helen.'

'And the fact that Father is worried sick because he got home to find himself locked out isn't your concern either!'

'I didn't intend that should happen. I assumed that your father would be at his club for the afternoon as he usually is. I didn't set out to cause Edward any distress. Now if you don't mind, I want to take that shower.' He glanced at the glass partition on the shower stall, then raised a mocking dark brow. 'Of course you are welcome to stay....'

Helen swung round on her heel and strode out of the room, steadfastly ignoring his taunting laughter. It would have afforded her the greatest pleasure to walk right out of the building, but what would that achieve? Jacob had said once that pride was a luxury she couldn't afford, and she was starting to understand what he'd meant. If she left then it wouldn't be just she who would suffer, but her father and Richard. It was all bound up together.

The minutes ticked by while Helen listened to the sound of the shower running and tried to work out what she should say, but when Jacob finally appeared she was still no closer to knowing what it should be. He studied her in silence for a moment, then walked over to his desk and flicked on the intercom to ask his secretary to bring in coffee. He then glanced calmly at Helen who was still standing in the middle of the room.

'Why don't you sit down? We can have coffee and see if we can find a solution to your problem.'

Helen glared at him with cold green eyes. 'I didn't come here on a social visit. And as for finding a solution that's simple: just give me the keys to the flat.'

Jacob sat down in one of the deep leather armchairs arranged at one end of the room, leaning comfortably back as he studied her with a faintly arrogant lift of his brows. 'And why should I do that, Helen? I told you the other day that I intended to take possession of the flat.'

'We've already been over that! It doesn't change the fact that Father and I have nowhere to live.'

'Nor does it alter the fact that that is no longer my problem.' He broke off as Annette tapped on the door and brought in the coffee, waiting until she had poured it and left before continuing. 'Nor, I imagine, does it change Richard's situation much.'

Helen sank down on to a chair, her legs suddenly too weak to support her. 'Would you really sack him, Jacob? It's such a dreadfully vicious thing to do, to hit at him because you can't have your way.'

His mouth thinned but his voice remained level. 'That seems a rather dramatic description of what I must do. I don't enjoy the thought of it, but it makes sense.'

'Sense? You are going to destroy Richard's career because of some feud you have with me and my family!' Her voice was hoarse, temper simmering in the depths of her green eyes, yet Jacob seemed unmoved by her anger.

'It makes sense to ensure that every person I employ remains loyal to me, Helen. And how could I be confident of Richard's loyalty once you tell him what has happened?' He shrugged as he picked up his cup and sipped the coffee. 'Naturally, Richard will be torn and that is a risk I cannot afford to take. I will not take any risks with Hunt Electronics. So from my point of view I am merely minimising any risks to safeguard the company.'

'You know that's all lies, Jacob. Lies, lies and more lies! You wouldn't have offered Richard the job if it hadn't been for his friendship with me!'

'I think you do Richard an injustice, Helen. He is extremely capable. It is just unfortunate that our present situation dictates this kind of action.' Jacob set his cup back on the tray then looked back at her in a way which made the blood start to swirl along her veins. What had she hoped to achieve by coming here? Had she really imagined that she could appeal to his better nature, that his attitude would change? If that was what she'd been hoping for then she was doomed to disappointment, because there wasn't a hint of softening in those hard blue eyes, no trace of any human emotion like compassion. Jacob Hunt had set out to achieve an objective and that was all that mattered. It made her feel suddenly afraid.

'I——'

He cut her off as though he hadn't noticed her attempt to speak, his deep voice holding a note which made a shudder run through her like ice. Unconsciously, Helen held her breath, listening to the pounding beat of her heart which sounded so loud that Jacob must hear it too, but even that thought didn't deaden the impact of his words.

'You hold the solution to it all in your hands, Helen. Marry me, and not only will your father's future comfort and security be assured but Richard's career also.'

It was hard to speak, hard to force any words out, but she finally managed it as she jumped to her feet. 'No! You must be mad, Jacob, to imagine I would ever agree to it. I hate you; all I want out of life is to find a way to get even with you!'

'And I am offering you the perfect opportunity.' He stood up, big and powerful as he stared down at her. 'Marry me, Helen, and you will get to know me better than any other human being does, learn all my weaknesses, all my vulnerabilities. Imagine then how you could wreak your revenge.' He caught her cold hands and drew her closer, his eyes burning as they searched her shocked ones. 'Marry me, Helen, not out of love but another emotion just as strong—hate.'

His voice seemed to fill her head, the words weaving through the fear to make a horrible kind of sense. She would never be free of Jacob. No matter where she went or what she did, he would always affect her life in some way. Yet if she married him then she could find some way to make him pay for all the heartache and pain he had caused her family. Know thine enemy! Well, she would learn all she could about him and in that way ultimately destroy him!

'Yes.' Her voice was clear as she stared up at him. It held no note of hesitation. She might come to regret this decision but he might regret her making it even more! 'Yes, I shall marry you, Jacob, and believe me I shall make sure that you regret the day you asked me for the rest of your life!'

Something flickered in his eyes, an emotion so raw that it seemed to scorch her before his lids lowered as he bent and touched his lips to hers in a kiss which was nothing but a sealing of their agreement, yet Helen drew back at once, oddly shaken by the feel of his mouth on hers.

'I shall make all the arrangements as soon as possible, Helen. I see no reason to wait, do you?'

She shrugged, trying to rid herself of the lingering and deeply disturbing feel of his mouth on hers. 'Not really. Whenever you like, Jacob. I don't care. However, I do have one or two provisos which will need to be met before the actual ceremony.'

'And they are?' He sounded more amused than concerned as he walked over to his desk and rested against the edge of it.

'Just that I want an agreement drawn up and signed by you that Father will be provided for for the rest of his life and that Richard's job will be secure for——' she pursed her lips as she deliberated '—two years.'

'You have my word, Helen.'

She shook her head, the fiery waves swirling around her shoulders. 'Not good enough, I'm afraid. I want it in writing, Jacob, and I want it well before the date of the wedding so that my solicitor can go through it with a fine-tooth comb!'

He laughed aloud. 'Don't you trust me to keep my word, Helen?'

'I don't trust you—period!' Her eyes skimmed his lean figure with icy contempt. 'Of course if you are starting to have second thoughts as to the wisdom of all this then I can't say that I blame you. You do know what you are letting yourself in for?'

'Oh, I know, Helen.' His eyes skimmed down her slender body, his voice dropping to a level which made the words strum along her nerves, making them tingle with heady awareness. 'This is something I have wanted for a long time.'

She didn't enjoy her reaction to that lazy look, the sound of that deeply sensuous voice. It sparked an anger aimed partly at him but even more at herself. 'Then you only have yourself to blame, don't you, Jacob, when it all turns into the nightmare it's destined to be—for you, that is?'

'Nightmare? Is that how you think it will turn out?'

'How else? In fact, I'm so sure that I want another clause adding to our agreement, stating that if you decide you want to end our marriage then you will still fulfil your obligations under the terms of the contract.' She laughed suddenly. 'I wonder how long it will take before you've had enough? Six months? Less? This could turn out to be one of the most profitable decisions I have ever made!'

He straightened away from the desk, walking slowly across the room to stop in front of her. Helen could smell the faint clean tang of soap and shampoo from his recent shower, see the dampness of his black hair which was just starting to curl at the back of his head, thick and springy and so vitally alive. It made heat swirl inside her and she looked away so that Jacob could see no hint of it, but he calmly slid his hand against her cheek and turned her face back to his.

'It won't be six months, Helen, nor even ten. When you marry me it will be a lifetime's commitment. Understand?'

She drew away from him, trying hard to keep the fear from her voice. 'Time will tell, Jacob.'

'It will indeed.' He turned away, sitting down behind the desk before glancing up at her. 'So now that we have everything agreed, that appears to be that. I'm sure you will understand when I tell you that I'm afraid I can't spare you any more time today. I shall be in touch about the arrangements.' He opened a folder lying on the desk, then looked up again as he felt in the pocket of his jacket. He tossed her a set of keys, his blue eyes betraying little as he watched her catch them automatically. 'These are for the flat, Helen. Tell your father that there is no need to worry. Everything has been sorted out satisfactorily.'

She flushed at the cool irony in his voice but made no comment as she walked to the door. Then she stopped, struck by a sudden unpalatable thought. 'Richard— what—what shall I tell him?'

'You could try the truth, I imagine. However, I am not totally unfeeling, Helen. I can appreciate that it could be embarrassing to have to tell him that you are about to marry his boss in the near future.' He shrugged dismissively, picking up a pen from the desk and making a note on the paper he was reading. 'Leave it to me. I shall tell him.'

'Jacob, you will...'

'Be kind? Was that what you were about to say?' All of a sudden she could sense anger in him, yet she couldn't understand what had caused it. Jacob now had everything he had ever wanted. He was the victor, to a point, in their battle so why should she sense that something had roused him to fury? However, before she could work out the puzzle he continued, his voice betraying little but a faint amusement which made her hate him more than ever. 'Don't worry, Helen, my love. I can afford to be generous to a loser.'

He bent his head as he turned back to his work. Helen left the office, smiling vaguely at Richard as she hurried towards the door to the corridor.

'Helen? What is going on here?'

Richard followed her into the corridor, bewilderment clearly apparent from his tone. Helen slowed to a reluctant halt and turned back to face him, forcing a stiff little smile to her face.

'Richard, this is rather awkward to explain. Perhaps— perhaps it would be better if you waited until Jacob had a word with you.'

He frowned as he walked closer to her. 'What has Jacob Hunt got to do with anything? Look, if I've upset you in any way then——'

'No! Honestly, Richard, it hasn't anything to do with you upsetting me.'

'Then what is this all about?' He glanced around, his eyes narrowing suspiciously. 'In fact, what *are* you doing here in the first place? I didn't know that you knew Hunt that well, didn't think you would want to from the few comments you've made about the man.'

'Jacob and I—well, we have known each other for some years now,' she admitted lamely, wondering what to do. How could she just come out and tell Richard that she had agreed to marry Jacob? It seemed so brutal.

'I knew you two were acquainted, Helen. After all, you both come from the same area, and Jacob did buy your family's house and business, but I didn't realise you knew him well enough to come visiting!'

There was a hard note in Richard's usually quiet tone, and Helen glanced almost helplessly around her. The last thing she wanted was an argument here.

'Look, Richard, I really don't think this is the place to start a discussion. Let's agree to leave this until later, shall we?'

'No, we shan't.' He caught her by the arm, his pleasant face unusually harsh. 'I want to know what's going on!'

'I think you should tell him, Helen. There doesn't seem any point in keeping it a secret any longer.'

She hadn't realised there was a door leading directly from Jacob's office into the corridor, and started nervously when he spoke just behind her. She swung round, her eyes widening as she spotted Jacob standing in the doorway watching them. He smiled thinly, his eyes holding a dangerous glimmer as they dropped to where Richard's hand was still fastened around her arm. Richard immediately let her go and stepped back a pace, although there was still more than a trace of belligerence on his face.

'I think it would be better if you both came into my office. It will be far less public.' Jacob disappeared inside the room, leaving Helen no alternative but to follow him.

He closed the door, then leant back against it, studying Richard's set face before his gaze settled on Helen.

'Have you told him yet?'

Helen shook her head, feeling colour swimming into her face at the sheer embarrassment of the situation. She was extremely fond of Richard and the last thing she wanted was to cause him any distress, but it seemed events were out of her hands now.

'Told me what? Look, Jacob, I know something is going on and I want to hear what it is!' He paused, his face going suddenly pale. 'Did you ask Helen here to help soften the blow when—when you fire me?'

Jacob smiled slightly, his eyes catching Helen's and holding them for a moment which was full of meaning. She dropped her gaze away from his mocking one, feeling sick. 'No, I can honestly say that your job is guaranteed safe for the next couple of years, Richard.'

Richard sagged visibly with relief, but was still obviously confused. 'I am delighted to hear it, but I still don't understand what's happening.'

'I can appreciate that. I'm afraid this has been rather unexpected for us too, hasn't it, Helen?' Jacob walked over to her and slid his arm around her shoulders as he smiled down at her in a way which made her palm itch to slap his arrogant face. Didn't he understand how awful this would be for Richard? Didn't he care? Apparently not, because he continued in the same unapologetic tone, 'Helen has just agreed to become my wife.'

'Your—Helen?' The shock on Richard's face was almost her undoing. Helen took a half-step towards him, then stopped when Jacob's hand tightened around her shoulder. She glanced up into his deep blue eyes, seeing the determination etched so clearly in their depths, and knew she had to go along with what he'd said.

'It's true, Richard,' she said gently, hating herself for inflicting pain on the other man. 'I know it must come as a shock for you and I'm sorry. I—I didn't want you to find out this way.'

'It doesn't matter how I found out! In heaven's name, Helen, why didn't you tell me before?' Richard made an obvious effort to control himself. 'I just wish you had warned me that something like this was on the cards, then perhaps I wouldn't feel such a fool!'

'Richard, I...'

'I think I just explained that neither Helen nor I foresaw this happening. I don't see any need to go into further explanations.' Jacob's fingers still bit into her flesh, hard yet strangely reassuring now, and unconsciously Helen took a step towards him, flushing when she saw that Richard had immediately noticed. She felt dreadful for hurting him this way, even though there had been no promises made, no commitments. Had she always known in her heart that Richard wasn't the man for her? Perhaps, but that didn't help soften the blow he'd just been dealt. And the worst thing was that she was powerless to explain to him the real reasons she was marrying Jacob.

She stared at Richard in silent apology but he ignored her, his smile tinged with bitterness as he turned to Jacob. 'Then there doesn't seem anything left to say. Forgive me for not offering congratulations, but from my point of view this is hardly a cause for celebration.'

'I can appreciate that. However, if it will be any consolation to you, Richard, then you have my word that I shall do everything in my power to make Helen happy and not regret her decision to marry me.' Jacob betrayed little by that cool statement yet Helen felt her temper rise. She already regretted agreeing to marry him and she had only made the decision minutes ago!

It was on the tip of her tongue to tell him that she had changed her mind when she caught his gaze and all the fire went out of her. If she did that, then they would all be back to square one. Richard might never find out, but one of the reasons for this marriage was to save him from whatever Jacob had planned!

Suddenly she couldn't stand it a moment longer, and pulled away from Jacob's hold, walking swiftly to the door before glancing back with tears shimmering in her eyes. 'I'm sorry, Richard. I hope that one day you will be able to accept what I've done.'

She hurried into the corridor but got no further than a few yards before Jacob stopped her, his face thunderous as he glared down at her. 'And what was that supposed to mean? If you imagine that I am going to allow you to tell Jackson the reasons for our marriage, then think again! Whatever you and he had going is past—understand?'

Helen stared up at him, refusing to back down in the face of his anger. 'Don't worry. I have no intention of telling Richard the truth! He wouldn't thank me for it. He has more pride than that. Richard is a decent, honest man; he wouldn't understand the kind of rules you play by, but I do! Now, if you will excuse me, I want to leave.'

'Certainly. Don't let me detain you any longer, Helen. But remember what I just said. This agreement is strictly between ourselves.' He smiled thinly, his blue eyes icy as they skimmed her face, the proud tilt of her head.

'You wouldn't enjoy the way I make my displeasure felt if you chose to be indiscreet, Helen.'

'I'm sure I wouldn't. That at least is one thing we can agree on, Jacob.' She forced a brilliant smile, her eyes hating him. 'It might be the only thing, I imagine.'

'I think you are underestimating what we have going for us, my sweet.' He moved closer, blocking her path as he backed her against the wall and stopped so close that she breathed the scent of him into her lungs. It made her feel breathless and giddy, as though her whole body were suddenly filled with him. When he reached out and ran his finger lightly down her cheek, she flinched, her eyes enormous as they stared into his.

He smiled slowly, bending just a fraction closer until his face filled her vision, blocking out all sight of everything else. 'I imagine that you and I will find many things we can—agree on, Helen. Many levels where we can meet. It will be exciting testing that theory out.'

Helen closed her eyes, blanking out the sight of him, her whole body shaking in a reaction she couldn't hide. 'I hate you, Jacob,' she whispered, then repeated it more clearly as she opened her eyes and stared up at him. 'I hate you!'

He never even flinched, his face impassive before he suddenly stepped back. 'I'm sure you do. Now I think I had better get back to your "friend" Richard. There are a few things we need to make clear between us if I hope to keep that promise I made you about his job security.'

There was an edge to his voice which alarmed her. 'You won't go back on your word, Jacob? You won't try to push Richard into doing anything rash?'

'And jeopardise the agreement we've made?' He shook his head. 'I won't do that, Helen. I told you before that marrying you is something I have wanted for a long time now. I have no intention of losing something I have set my mind on having.'

He was gone before Helen could think of anything else to say. What a mess all this was: herself, father, Richard, all sucked into the trap Jacob had been laying all these years. Yet somehow she had to find a way to use it against him. Somehow she had to find a way to make Jacob Hunt regret every single thing he had done!

CHAPTER FOUR

THE noise was making Helen's head ache. Excusing herself from the group, she walked over to the entrance of the huge marquee which had been erected in the grounds of the house and drew in lungfuls of the cool night air.

The party had been Jacob's idea. Helen had merely gone along with it as she had gone along with all the other arrangements he had made this past week or so. If she had wondered why Jacob had chosen to give such a lavish event as this party, then she had soon had an answer once she'd arrived. Tonight Jacob intended to announce their forthcoming marriage, and as Helen had stood by his side to greet the guests she had recognised amongst them everyone who had been at that abruptly curtailed dinner party.

Rumour had been rife since that night but it hadn't seemed to bother Jacob, and why should it? He had so neatly turned the tables on her that what she'd planned to do seemed almost laughable now. And once he announced their wedding later in the evening, then that would quash any further talk and speculation as to why she had acted the way she had, giving everyone something fresh to focus their interest on. Helen Sinclair marrying Jacob Hunt—she could almost feel the shock-waves that would send out, yet she was less concerned with people's reaction than she was about the utter finality of it. Once Jacob made that announcement then there would be no going back!

She glanced across the crowd as a sudden panic claimed her at the realisation, and her eyes met Jacob's. Tonight was the first time she had seen him since that day in his office, although they had spoken frequently by telephone. Now Helen felt the full impact of him hit her with a force which sent her senses reeling. Even in the elegant, sophisticated dinner clothes he looked tough and uncompromising, his blue eyes glittering with a steely determination. She had agreed to this marriage to get even with him, yet how could she hope to do that? How could she beat a man who had fought and won so many battles, who used whatever means it took to get what he wanted? She must have been mad! For the past few days she had tried to tell herself that she had made the right decision, closing her mind to the nagging fears, but now seeing him again made her realise what a fool she had been.

Fear came coldly and swiftly, steeling any rational thoughts. All she knew right then was that she had to get away from Jacob and this foolish commitment she had made before it was too late. No one noticed as she slipped out of the marquee and ran across the lawn, no one apart from Jacob, that was. Would he follow her?

The thought lent speed to her flying feet as she lifted up the hem of her emerald silk taffeta gown and raced towards her car. She slid inside, crushing the skirt as she bunched it up to close the door. The key was still in the ignition where she had left it, and she turned it with shaking fingers, but before she had time to start the engine the door was opened and another hand closed over hers to switch it off.

'Going somewhere, Helen?'

Her heart leapt into her throat. There was no way that she could answer, no way that she could even turn to look at Jacob who was standing beside the car. It was only when he suddenly bent and lifted her over into the passenger seat before sliding himself behind the wheel that she reacted.

'What are you doing?' she demanded shrilly, and saw his amused look as he started the engine and turned the small car down the drive.

'You seemed eager to leave, my sweet, so naturally I'm coming with you. Imagine our guests' surprise if they discovered you had left just as I was about to make the announcement of our marriage. They might start to wonder what exactly was going on.' He cast her a harsh look, his blue eyes filled with determination. Jacob would allow nothing and no one to thwart his plans, and she'd been a fool to imagine she could—just yet! To hit back at Jacob she had to be patient and discover all his weak spots.

She laughed softly, forcing the thunderous pounding of her heart to slow. 'Are you so sure they won't start wondering about it anyway, Jacob? Do you really imagine those people will think this marriage of ours was founded in heaven?'

He shrugged lightly as he turned the car on to the main road which led through the village. 'Who knows? However, I'm sure that time will tell how successful it has been.'

'That sounds almost as though you have high hopes for us. How touching, Jacob, although I'm sure you're doomed to disappointment.' She sighed softly as she smoothed the emerald silk so that it lay in a shimmering waterfall over her legs. 'The one thing I would never have taken you for was a sentimentalist.'

'I doubt you know anything at all about me, Helen. Oh, I'm sure you think you know me, but you could find the reality far different from the picture you have built inside your head.'

There was something in his deep voice which sent a sudden unease sliding through her, and she shifted in the seat. She *knew* what Jacob was like and she had no intention of altering her views. 'I doubt that. I've had years to form my opinion, so I don't imagine that I shall be in for any major surprises.'

'Years?' He laughed harshly, turning the car into a lay-by and switching off the engine. 'Oh, come on, Helen, don't exaggerate!'

'It isn't an exaggeration, Jacob. You were seventeen when you first moved into the village, and even then I had a good idea what you were like!'

'Did you?' He laughed in a way which sent a flow of heat through her limbs. 'You didn't understand the first thing about me, sweet little Helen. That's why you gave me all those half terrified looks from those huge green eyes.' He lifted her chin, his fingers cool against her flesh. In the dim light from the dashboard his face was shadowy, indistinct. Only his eyes seemed clear, deep and glittering as they studied her so intently that she wanted to turn away and hide in case he saw things in her head she herself didn't know were there.

'Don't be ridiculous, Jacob. You're imagining things.'

'No. I knew how you felt about me, Helen, even then. You were both scared and fascinated. I was something outside your safe, secure little world, an unknown quantity and in a way that has never changed because you have always been too scared to get close enough to discover the truth.'

'I—no!' She twisted away from the disturbing contact with his fingers, her green eyes spitting sparks at him. 'Don't flatter yourself, Jacob Hunt! There was nothing at all fascinating about you. You were trouble from the day you set foot in the village. You caused more fights than there had ever been. Do you imagine I didn't hear about them?'

'And naturally I was to blame for them all.' There was a faint weariness in his tone now rather than anger. 'Nobody ever gave me the benefit of the doubt, did they, Helen? No one asked themselves if just possibly I might have been the victim?'

'You—a victim? That's a joke, Jacob. You were far too tough to be anyone's victim!'

'I imagine I gave that impression. After all, I'd had years to learn how to hide my feelings.' He saw her start of surprise because he smiled, and Helen felt something ache inside her at the bitter sadness of it.

'What do you mean?'

'Simply that my life had been one long round of other people's prejudices. My mother was a proud woman; she didn't see why she should lie just to conform to other people's views. I never knew my father. He and Mother were never married and he left her when I was just a baby.

'Her crime was to be an unmarried woman doing her best to care for her child. She never asked or expected anything from anyone, but unfortunately people didn't see things the way she did.' He leant back in the seat, his expression distant as he looked back on a past Helen could only barely imagine. 'I soon learned to stand up for myself, Helen. It was a case of having to. Nowadays there isn't the same stigma to being illegitimate but, despite its being the wonderful swinging sixties when I was born, most people hadn't changed the views they had held for years.'

'The story was that your mother was a widow,' Helen said softly, and saw him grimace.

'But it didn't last long, did it? Mother had grown tired of all the hostility, so when we moved here that's what she told everyone, but nobody really believed her, I imagine.'

Helen flushed, strangely uncomfortable with the truth of that flat statement. 'You have to remember that the village was a tight-knit community. Old-fashioned values were even more deeply entrenched here than many other places. They still are, in fact.'

'So I discovered.' He sat up straight, his face suddenly cold and hard. 'If there was trouble, Helen, I didn't go looking for it. I didn't have to when every youth in the neighbourhood was keen to push it into my face!'

She knew it was the truth. Jacob had aroused feelings and passions in people from the moment he had arrived in the small community. Yet that still didn't excuse what he had done later.

'So because people were prejudiced towards you, you set out to teach them a lesson? Is that it, Jacob? And who better to be your targets than my family? We represented everything you had learned to hate!'

'If that is the way you choose to see it, then who am I to argue, Helen?' He started the engine, then gave her a cool little smile as he turned the car back the way they had come. 'It's hard to change people's opinions, I've found, but eventually most have to concede the truth.'

'Meaning that I might alter my view of you because of what you have just told me?' She shook her head, then brushed from her cheek a few wisps of hair which had slipped from the elegant chignon, using the few seconds it took to collect herself. Had her opinion of Jacob altered slightly? She didn't want to think it had, wanted even less for him to think it! 'Sorry, Jacob. Touching though your little tale was, it will take more than that to convince me that beneath that tough-as-nails exterior lies the real soft you trying to get out!'

His hands tightened on the steering-wheel, the only sign of annoyance at the deliberate taunt. 'Then obviously I shall have to try harder to change your views.' He laughed suddenly, the sound rippling around the car. 'Still, isn't that what marriage is all about, darling? Discovering new things about one another?'

'There is nothing new I need or want to discover about you, Jacob, apart from how to make you pay for all you've done! And believe me, I shall make that my number one concern. Does it make you wonder if you may have made a rather large error of judgement by handing me such a wonderful opportunity? You might come to regret it very quickly!'

'Think so?' He lifted her hand from where it was lying on her knee and raised it to his lips, pressing a slow kiss against her knuckles. 'Fortunately I don't share your doubts, Helen. To my mind I am about to achieve my ultimate goal. You were the one thing missing, sweet, the one thing I had always set my heart on having.'

There was something in his voice which made her pulse jerk in reaction to it, and she dragged her hand away from his grasp, afraid that he would feel it. It was nerves, that was all, a very natural reaction to the thought of the coming wedding. Yet there was no way she could ignore the heat curling inside her, the faint tremor in her body. Jacob disturbed her in ways she didn't want to think about—ever! She must never forget why she was marrying him, out of hatred and a desire for revenge. Indeed his own feelings towards her had to be in a similar vein. Why else had he spent these past few years destroying everything she held dear?

The thought steadied her, steeling her resolve when she needed it most. 'Isn't there a saying about being careful what you wish for because you might just get it?' She laughed softly. 'It could so easily be applied to this very situation!'

He cast her a slow look, his face inscrutable in the shadows. 'It could, and not just towards my wishes. What about your wishes, Helen, your dream of getting even with me for all those wrongs I have supposedly done you?'

'There is no "suppose" about it! You set out to destroy everything my family had, so what else could you call it but wrong?'

He shook his head, a heavy lock of black hair falling on to his forehead. He pushed it back with a steady hand, calmly turning the car in through the gates marking the driveway to the house. Even though Helen could sense the anger burning in him now, he was still in control. That was one of the most terrifying things about Jacob, that tightly leashed control he held on his feelings. Everything he did was carefully planned and just as carefully executed. To beat him she would have to learn to emulate that ironclad restraint, but it wouldn't be easy.

'I won't argue with you, Helen. Not now when there are people waiting for us, watching and judging our every look, our every word.' He drew the car to a halt and switched off the engine, then turned off the lights, plunging them into a darkness barely relieved by the silvery glow of the moonlight. From the direction of the marquee came the strains of music, as the band Jacob had hired played for the entertainment of his guests. What a farce it all was, the party, the coming announcement!

Her eyes glittered as she half turned in her seat to face him, contempt laced through her voice. 'Do you really imagine that people are going to believe this marriage is for real? Do you think they are going to look at us and see two people so madly in love?' She laughed a trifle shrilly, reaching for the door-handle, but Jacob was too quick for her.

His hand closed around her bare arm as he stopped her from leaving. Helen turned to tell him to let her go, then found the words wouldn't come as he drew her closer to him and held her there so that she could feel the steely strength of his chest pressing against her soft breasts, feel the warmth of his body through the thin white silk shirt.

'Perhaps you're right, Helen. Thank you for warning me. At least it gives me a chance to do something about it.'

She wasn't prepared when he suddenly bent and kissed her. The shock of the contact flowed through her like fire, scorching a trail of devastation through her body. All the brusque words melted under the deeply sensuous assault. His lips seemed to draw the strength from her as they clung to hers, so warm and tender that she responded instinctively to the kiss, her own lips giving back the response he sought. Jacob wasn't a gentle man but

his kiss was achingly gentle, and that was her undoing.
If he had tried to force her to respond then Helen would
have had no difficulty in refusing, yet she was helpless
against this slow, seductive, and deeply disturbing assault on her senses.

When he drew back and slowly let her go it took
minutes to rid herself of the drugging effect his mouth
had left behind. She stared at him in silence, shock
evident in the wide, stormy emerald of her eyes, the
shallowness of her breathing. Slowly he reached out and
smoothed his thumb across her mouth, watching the way
her lips parted slightly at the contact before he drew his
hand back and smiled coolly at her. 'Perfect, Helen.
That's just the expression people would expect to see on
the face of a woman who has just spent a few tender
minutes alone with her future husband.'

The mocking taunt broke the spell. Helen sucked in
air so fast that her lungs ached as she glared into his
amused face. 'It would take a better actress than I could
ever be to convince people I care about you, Jacob
Hunt!'

'Oh, I think you underestimate your ability, Helen.
If I didn't know better you might even have fooled me
just now.' He smiled meaningfully, then climbed out of
the car and waited for her to join him. 'However, I do
not want any more talk, Helen. If I hear any rumours
that our relationship isn't all it is meant to be, then I
might find that I have to renege on our agreement.' He
took her arm and steered her towards the marquee,
drawing her to a halt as he stared down into her face.
'You do understand, Helen?'

'Perfectly.' She smiled up at him with a biting contempt. 'I shall play my part to the very best of my ability,

Jacob, not to make things easier for you but because I have my own reasons for wanting this marriage to take place!' She paused, then added deliberately, 'However, I don't intend to allow any repeat of tonight's episode. I don't need any "acting" lessons, thank you very much!'

She walked ahead of him, doing her best as she circulated among the guests to put what had happened out of her mind. Yet each time she looked up and found Jacob watching her she couldn't prevent the fear at the awareness in his eyes. Jacob had kissed her for his own very clear reasons but that didn't explain why she had responded. And the worst thing was that Jacob was wondering about it too!

There were lights on in the flat when Helen arrived home. Jacob had offered to drive her back and arrange to have her car returned to her the following day, but she had curtly refused. She didn't want to be alone with him again, to see that awareness in his eyes. It was something she wanted to work through by herself and understand. There had to be a rational reason why she had responded to his kiss, yet all through the evening, as she had circulated among the guests and fielded their curious questions about the wedding, she hadn't been able to find it.

Now she fixed a determined smile to her mouth as she walked into the sitting-room and found her father there reading. He looked up when he heard her, taking off his glasses and setting his book aside. 'Ah, Helen. How did it go, then? Was it a nice party?'

Helen dropped her bag on to the sofa, then tossed her black velvet evening cloak after it, trying to disguise the nervousness she felt so as not to arouse Edward Sinclair's suspicions. 'It seemed to go very well. I think Jacob was pleased, anyway. He—he announced that we're getting married.'

Her father nodded. 'Yes, he told me that was what he intended to do.' He must have seen her surprise because he smiled. 'Jacob very formally asked for your hand in marriage when he paid me a visit the other day while you were out, darling. It may be old-fashioned but I must say that I respected him for paying me that courtesy.'

Helen looked away, not wanting her father to see what she thought about Jacob's consideration. He'd never mentioned a thing about it to her, but wasn't that typical of him? He made his plans and carried them through exactly as he saw fit!

'You are sure that this marriage is what you want, aren't you, Helen?' Edward Sinclair's voice held a note of real concern, and hastily Helen strove to push her feelings aside. Her father had been looking much better since he had found out about the wedding and all that it entailed regarding his future, and she didn't want to undo all the good work.

'Of course!' She laughed lightly. 'What a strange question, Father.'

'Not really. You must admit that it has all been rather sudden. One minute you and Jacob are at daggers drawn and the next you are planning on getting married.' He glanced down at the book he held, then looked back at her steadily. 'I wouldn't like to think that you might be doing this for the wrong reasons, Helen.'

She jumped to her feet, uncomfortable under the look. She walked over to the window and stared down at the city street, watching a car travelling slowly along the road before it drew to a halt. From this distance it looked remarkably like Jacob's car, and she drew in a quick exasperated little breath. Now she was starting to imagine she was seeing him!

'Helen?'

She jumped when her father spoke again to draw her attention back to the fact that she hadn't answered his question. Letting the curtain drop back into place, she turned to him with a determined smile. 'My reasons for marrying Jacob are all the right ones, believe me, father.'

Her voice held the ring of conviction and the worry faded from his face. He got up slowly and crossed the room, kissing her lightly on the cheek. 'Good. That eases my mind, dear. Now I think I shall go on to bed, seeing that you are home safe and sound.' He gave a faintly sheepish smile. 'I know, you're a grown woman now, but a father can't help worrying.'

Helen kissed him back with real affection. 'Well, don't. I can take care of myself.'

'I'm sure you can, and the things you can't handle I'm sure Jacob can take care of for you. He's an extremely capable man, Helen, and I couldn't have chosen anyone better to look after you when I'm gone.'

He started towards the door but Helen couldn't let him leave without explaining that strange statement. 'You sound as though you admire Jacob, Father, but doesn't it bother you about the house and the business?'

The elderly man stopped and turned slowly to face her, his lined face holding just the faintest hint of regret. 'What does bother me is the fact that I couldn't do what Jacob has managed to do.' He shrugged wearily. 'I was never cut out to be a businessman. Your mother was better at that kind of thing than I ever was. After she died then I'm afraid things seemed to get on top of me. If Jacob hadn't stepped in, then...' He stopped abruptly, smiling. 'But I'm sure you know all about that. Goodnight, darling.'

Helen watched him go with a frown puckering her smooth brow. Edward Sinclair had sounded almost *grateful* to Jacob, but how could that be? Jacob had taken away everything the family had ever owned, so that was hardly a basis for gratitude! She turned back to the window, resting her hot forehead against the cool glass as she tried to make sense out of it all, but it was impossible to do that. Maybe she had imagined it, tiredness making her hear things that hadn't been there. The best thing she could do was go to bed and sleep, then see if it was any clearer in the morning.

She switched off the table lamp by the sofa, then walked over to the one on the small antique desk by the far window, jumping nervously as the telephone next to it suddenly rang. She snatched up the receiver at once, not wanting her father to be disturbed by what was probably a wrong number.

'Helen?'

There was no mistaking that deep, dark voice. Every pulse in Helen's body jumped, her breath catching at the unexpected sound of it, until she heard Jacob laugh softly, with a depth of meaning.

'Come on, sweet, I just know it's you. Not afraid to answer me, are you?'

'The day hasn't come when I would ever be afraid of speaking to you, Jacob Hunt! What do you want?'

'What a way to greet your fiancé. I'm cut to the quick, Helen.'

'If you rang to play ridiculous word games then I am sorry, Jacob. It's far too late to start a verbal fencing match with you!'

'Then maybe we should try speaking to each other in a completely different way.' His voice dropped an octave, smooth as satin as it hummed down the phone and made her whole body tingle with awareness. 'I just thought I would call you to wish you goodnight before you went to bed, my sweet. Pleasant dreams.'

Helen shook herself out of the sensual spell he was creating with his tone. 'How touching of you! My, my, Jacob, you really do put yourself into a role body and soul, don't you?'

He laughed deeply. 'Anything I set my mind to, Helen, I give it my full, undivided attention. Surely you must know that?'

She wasn't sure she liked the idea of being at the receiving end of Jacob's "attention"! 'If by that you mean you are single-minded and ruthless, then yes, I do know that very well! Now if that is all——'

He cut her off, his tone a shade harder now. 'Not quite. I forgot to tell you that I shall pick you up around twelve tomorrow to go to my solicitors to sign that contract. I believe that your solicitor was quite happy with it?'

Helen couldn't help the flush which stained her cheeks. Although there had been little comment from her solicitor when she had explained about the pre-nuptial agreement, she had sensed a certain well-concealed surprise. 'Yes, he could find no problems with it.'

'Good. Another thing out of the way.' Jacob's tone was bland, so why did she have the sudden and quite inexplicable feeling that he *knew* how embarrassed she felt?

Helen's blood began to boil at the thought, but before she could say anything he spoke again.

'So I shall see you tomorrow, Helen. Oh, and don't forget to switch that lamp off before you go to bed.'

He cut the connection, leaving Helen staring down at the receiver in confusion for a few seconds before she dropped it back on to its rest and ran to the window just in time to see the car she'd noticed before pulling away from the kerb. It drew level with the street-lamp as it passed beneath the window and she had no difficulty in recognising Jacob before it roared away.

Helen turned away from the window, automatically going back to switch off the lamp. Her hand rested on the switch for a moment, confusion clearly etched on her face before, with a determined flick of her fingers, she switched it off and plunged the room into darkness.

She had no idea what sort of game Jacob was playing by following her home, and frankly she had no intention of standing there trying to work it out. She was going to bed and going to put Jacob Hunt right out of her mind for the rest of the night. What a pity she couldn't put him right out of her life as well!

CHAPTER FIVE

HELEN was ready and dressed in a dark green wool suit and cream silk blouse, with her hair caught back from her face by two tortoiseshell combs, and with her temper hovering just a degree or two below boiling point, when Jacob arrived the next morning.

Despite all her steely assertions, she had spent the night thinking about him, strange, disturbing dreams which once she had woken she had determinedly tried to erase from her mind. But just the sight of him standing at the door, immaculate as ever in a navy suit with a pale blue shirt, brought them all flooding back.

She stalked back into the sitting-room and picked up her bag, willing herself to stay calm. They had been just dreams, that was all, strange, unsettling fantasies which had no basis in fact. Yet she couldn't help but remember the sheer sensuality of them.

'Someone seems to have got out of the wrong side of bed this morning.' Jacob followed her into the room, walking calmly over to the window to push back the curtain in much the same way as she had the night before, and Helen felt her temper warm just one degree more.

'I was perfectly fine until you arrived,' she said sweetly. 'I wonder if that could be any indication of what is wrong with me?'

He smiled as he glanced back at her. 'Temper, temper, Helen. What is the matter with you, my sweet? Surely you aren't worried about signing this contract?' He paused deliberately, big and powerful as he stood there and watched her with those dark blue eyes which seemed to see so much. Helen shifted uncomfortably, sliding the strap of her bag over her shoulder.

'Why should I be worried about it? It was my suggestion after all, Jacob.' She shrugged lightly as she started towards the door, but suddenly he was there before her, barring her way.

'Then if it isn't that, Helen, what is it?' He studied her face, his eyes lingering on the faint blue shadows beneath her green eyes, mute testimony of the restless night she'd had. 'You look tired. Didn't you sleep well?'

His voice sounded so soft and vibrant that a shiver ran through her and she looked away, terrified of what he might see. He couldn't know why her night had been so restless, couldn't see inside his head all the images which haunted her: Jacob bending to kiss her, his blue eyes glittering with a wild excitement; Jacob holding her in his arms as he stroked her body; Jacob moving over her to...

She blanked the images from her mind, pushing past him to walk out of the door. She was shaking all over, her body strung so tightly that she felt the smallest wrong move would make her shatter into hundreds and thousands of tiny pieces. It took every scrap of strength she possessed to stand waiting for him to join her, when what she felt like doing was running away and hiding.

'If I didn't sleep well then I have you to blame for that, don't I?' She took the key from her bag to double-lock the front door, inwardly cursing herself when she saw the betraying trembling of her hands.

Jacob calmly took the key from her and locked the door, then caught her hand, his fingers warm and steady as they closed over hers. 'Then I must apologise.' His mouth quirked attractively, his blue eyes very dark as they met hers. 'I never meant to cause you a sleepless night, Helen.'

Helen flushed, snatching her hand away from his as she dropped the key back into her bag. 'I find that hard to believe! What were you doing outside the flat if you weren't trying to *disturb* me?'

'So that's what this is all about.' He led the way to the lift, pressing the button to summon it before leaning against the wall as he studied her with a slow smile.

'Yes! I have no idea what you were up to last night, Jacob, but I don't like having you follow me!'

He straightened as the lift arrived, standing aside for her to precede him, but instead of pressing the button to take them down to the ground floor, he held the doors open. 'For your information, Helen, I wasn't up to anything at all other than ensuring that you arrived home safely.' There was a hard edge to his voice now and she glared at him, hating to hear that note of rebuke.

'And you expect me to believe that? Come on!'

'I don't expect you to believe anything I say, Helen. You've made it perfectly plain that you always suspect the worst from me, so why bother trying to convince you otherwise?' He released the doors, turning away from her as he pressed the button for the ground floor.

Helen stared at his broad back uncertainly. Had she done him an injustice by accusing him of having an ulterior motive? She wasn't sure that she liked the idea, nor the fact that she was beginning to have doubts herself. She knew what Jacob was like! Anything he did had a purpose. Yet it seemed strangely hard to convince herself this time.

In total silence she followed him out to where he had parked his big dark grey Mercedes, slipping into the passenger seat when he opened the door for her with a soft murmur of thanks. Yet when he slipped the key into the ignition to start the engine, she found she couldn't hold back the questions any longer.

'Was that really why you followed me, Jacob? Just to make sure I got home safely?'

There was a soft hesitation in her voice and he turned to look at her, his blue eyes very dark as they rested on her face for a long moment which seemed to be suddenly strangely tense. Helen looked away, wishing she hadn't spoken. There was just something in his eyes which made her feel suddenly uncertain, as though the ground had shifted beneath her feet to leave her off balance.

'Yes. I didn't like the thought of you making the journey by yourself at that time of night. Anything might have happened to you, Helen. And I didn't want to take that sort of a chance.'

His voice was strangely flat, devoid of the emotion she could sense lay behind that calm exterior, and Helen experienced a sudden crazy desire to make him admit what he really felt for once.

'So it was more a case of you safeguarding your interests, was it, Jacob?' She arched a slender brow, her tone deliberately challenging. 'After all, you have admitted several times that I'm the last thing you need to add to your list of achievements, so how awful if anything had happened to me to thwart all those plans?'

'How astute of you to realise it, my sweet. As you say, it would be galling to lose out now at the eleventh hour.' He started the engine, then flicked her one last look. 'I'm glad that you and I seem to understand one another so well, Helen.'

Helen turned away, staring blankly out of the car window as she tried to hide the bitter disappointment she felt. What a fool she was to imagine even for a moment that Jacob had followed her home because he had been genuinely worried about her! The only thing that Jacob Hunt worried about was ensuring his own rotten plans worked out as he wanted them to!

'Not sulking, are you, darling? I wonder why?' There was a faint but unmistakable amusement in his voice as he turned the sleek car into the flow of traffic. Helen snapped her lips tightly together, refusing to give vent to all the sharp answers struggling to get free. She didn't know what was worse, the mounting anger she felt at his single-mindedness or the strangely bitter sense of disappointment.

Jacob laughed softly, steering the car skilfully through the maze of traffic. 'Why do I get the idea that you're annoyed? Was my answer not quite what you had been hoping for, darling?'

'Don't "darling" me, Jacob Hunt! I don't need your sweet words or endearments. I know what you're really like, don't forget! I'm impervious to your particular brand of "charm"!'

'You really are annoyed.' There was satisfaction in his deep voice and in the slow look he gave her as they drew up outside the solicitor's office. Jacob cut the engine, then continued to study her until Helen could feel the colour swimming into her face. She unfastened her seatbelt, her fingers all clumsy thumbs under the intent stare, then visibly jumped when Jacob reached across and laid his hand over hers.

'I followed you home last night, Helen, because I was worried about you—*you*. Understand? It had nothing at all to do with any plans I may have made.'

She couldn't think what to say. Anything seemed to be fraught with danger. Just moments ago she had wanted to push Jacob into revealing his true feelings but now she knew that was the last thing she wanted!

She dragged her hands away and fumbled with the door-lock, then stopped when she heard his soft laugh.

'Does it scare you, Helen?'

She glanced back at him, her eyes not quite meeting his in case he saw the confusion she felt. 'I don't know what you mean and I am sure that now isn't the time to start a discussion about your possible motives. We shall be late.'

'What a little coward you really are, Helen. You're afraid to see what's staring you in the face.' He caught her arm and turned her back, his fingers cool on her heated flesh as he lifted her chin and made her meet his steady gaze. 'But one day soon, Helen, I'm going to make you face up to it all. I won't let you run away from the truth as you've been running for years now.'

She laughed harshly. '*I* must face up to the truth? That's rich, Jacob, coming from you! If you tried facing up to all the rotten things you have done then maybe we would find something to talk about, but don't hold your breath!'

Anger glittered in his eyes and his grip tightened before he made an obvious effort to control himself. He let her go and drew back as he unfastened his seatbelt, a faint amusement in the look he gave her. 'We'll soon see, I expect, but, as you so rightly said, we don't want to be late.'

He climbed out of the car, walking smoothly round to open Helen's door for her. She got out without a word, not waiting for him as she climbed the steps to the solicitor's office. She didn't want to think about what Jacob had meant, didn't want to think about anything but signing the contract. That and getting even with him was all she was interested in. Something warned her that playing truth games with Jacob could prove to be a huge mistake!

By the time that Jacob dropped her off outside the flat later that afternoon, Helen was exhausted. It had taken longer than she'd expected at the solicitor's office as the man had gone meticulously through every clause in the agreement. Helen couldn't decide which had been worse, seeing all the terms and conditions written down in indisputable black and white, or the man's fussy attention to every little detail. It had all seemed so *sordid* somehow, but there again no one could claim this forthcoming marriage had been made in heaven!

The lifts were all in use so Helen took the stairs, climbing to the second floor to pause outside the door while she found her key. Her father would be at his club as usual, reading the papers and chatting with his friends. Marrying Jacob meant that his routine wouldn't have to change now that he was going to remain in the flat. It was some sort of consolation at least.

'Helen.'

She gave a small cry of alarm and dropped her bag, her hand going instinctively to her throat to stem the wild leaping of her pulse as she suddenly recognised the man standing in the shadows. 'Richard! What are you doing here?'

He moved towards her, a faint frown on his face as he studied her. 'I had to come, Helen. I didn't mean to scare you, though.'

Helen shook her head, bending down to pick up the contents of her bag which had scattered halfway across the small hallway. 'It doesn't matter. I—I was just surprised to see you, that's all.'

'I'm sure you were.' There was more than a hint of bitterness in Richard's voice and Helen shot him a worried glance. She had not heard a word from him since that dreadful day in Jacob's office. Several times she had toyed with the idea of writing to him or even telephoning, but each time decided against it. What could she say, after all, apart from repeating her apologies for the way she had hurt him? She wasn't fool enough to think that Jacob hadn't meant that warning he had issued. She felt so guilty, but how could she make Richard understand that she had done everything with the best of intentions yet not tell him the truth?

She straightened up, forcing a smile as she unlocked the door. 'Would you like to come in, Richard? I could make us some coffee, perhaps.'

He nodded abruptly, walking past her to stop in the middle of the sitting-room and stare round in a way which made Helen strangely uneasy. 'I think I would prefer a drink, Helen.'

Helen paused in the middle of taking off her jacket, frowning at him. 'A drink? But you never drink in the middle of the day.'

'Then maybe it's about time I changed my habits.' He walked over to where the drinks were arranged on a small table and poured himself a generous measure of whisky, downing half of it before slamming the glass down on the tray with enough force to make Helen wince. 'Maybe I should change a lot of things about myself, Helen. What do you say?'

'I don't know what to say, if you want the truth.' She sat down on the edge of the sofa, her hands clasped in her lap. She had never seen Richard behaving like this before. It was completely out of character.

'Oh, I would like the truth all right, Helen. I would really like to hear it.' He picked up the glass and drank the rest of the whisky, then refilled it, staring at her over the top. 'So come on, Helen, why not tell me just what made you decide to marry a bastard like Jacob Hunt?'

Helen jumped to her feet, her face paling. 'Richard, I really don't know what's come over you coming here like this.'

'Don't you?' He laughed harshly, swallowing the whisky before tossing the glass carelessly back on to the tray. 'You treat me like some sort of fool for months, stringing me along, then dump me, and you want to know what's the matter with me.' He moved towards her so fast that Helen had no chance to avoid him as he caught her by the shoulders and shook her hard.

'It wasn't like that! Please, Richard, you must understand that I never intended to hurt you.' She tried to struggle free, but although Richard was only slightly built he was far too strong for her to escape him.

'You never intended to hurt me?' He mimicked her tone, his face faintly flushed. Helen could smell the whisky on his breath and wondered if he had been drinking before he'd come, yet it didn't add up to the picture she held of him. Dear, kind, patient Richard had never acted like this before! That he was acting this way now was all her fault.

The thought made her ache for the distress she had caused him, and she stopped struggling. 'No, I didn't. You must believe me, Richard.'

'Yet the minute I left the country you made a play for Jacob Hunt? Or did you wait until I had left? Maybe you were seeing him before then?' His eyes glittered with a feverish light, his hands bruising her shoulders through the thin cream blouse.

'No! You're wrong. Jacob and I—well, we explained the situation to you the other day.'

'Of course you did. It was all like some bolt out of the blue, you both suddenly discovered that you were in love? How wonderfully romantic it all sounds, yet I've been thinking about you and me, Helen, recently.' His hands slid down her spine to curve around her buttocks as he drew her closer. 'I always went along with what you wanted, didn't I? You set the rules and would never allow me to break them, but maybe that was a mistake. I can't imagine that Hunt was so patient and maybe I should take a leaf out of his book.'

His head came down, his lips bruising as he kissed her with a harsh brutality which terrified her. Helen struggled wildly, one part of her unable to believe what was happening. This was Richard! Dear, patient, Richard...

With a sudden surge of strength she pushed him away from her and ran to the front door, her only thought to get out of the flat before he caught her. Her fingers fumbled with the lock before she managed to get it open, then she gave a scream of shock as she found Jacob outside the door.

'Helen? What the hell is going on here?' Jacob's face was taut with anger, his blue eyes glittering as they

studied her pale face, the bruised swell of her mouth,
before they lifted and focused on the man who had followed her into the hall. Helen went cold at the expression on his face as he took a slow step past her.

'No! Jacob—Richard is just upset. He...'

He set her aside, barely sparing her a glance, his whole
attention focused on the fair-haired man who was
standing uncertainly a few feet away. 'Go into the sitting-
room, Helen, and leave this to me.'

'Jacob, you——'

He cut her off, his eyes like ice, his voice so harsh and
unrelenting that she flinched. 'Go!'

Without another word she ran into the sitting-room
and sank down on to the sofa, huddling into a tight little
ball, of pain and misery. She could hear voices outside
in the hall, but in a remarkably short time they stopped.
Yet when she heard footsteps crossing the room towards
her, she couldn't look up. She knew who they belonged
to, of course. Richard would never have stood a chance
against the fury she had witnessed on Jacob's face just
now.

'Here, drink this. You look as though you need it.'
He held a glass out to her containing a small measure
of brandy, but Helen shook her head.

'No, I don't want it.'

He swore softly, dropping down beside her on the sofa
and turning her to face him while he held the glass to
her lips. 'I said drink it. You look as though you're going
to pass out at any minute, from the colour of you.'

Helen took a tiny sip, then winced as she felt it sting
the inside of her lip. Tentatively she ran the tip of her
finger across the sore spot, surprised to find that it was
bleeding. She looked up at Jacob in shock and knew

that if she lived to be a hundred she would never forget the expression on his face just then. He looked as though he could happily commit murder, his face set into rigid lines, his eyes so dark with fury that they appeared black. Without a word he got up and Helen could hear him running water before he came back with a cloth and handed it to her.

'That should take the swelling down although it's going to be sore for a day or two. I wish to God I'd followed my instincts and given Jackson a taste of his own medicine instead of just throwing him out!'

Helen held the cloth to her mouth, closing her eyes to hold back the tears. She had never felt so ashamed in her whole life. All this had been her fault; she had driven Richard to act so completely out of character. Tears slid from under her closed lids and she heard Jacob give a rough exclamation as he took the cloth out of her hand then drew her to her feet, holding her close against him as he stroked her hair and murmured a string of meaningless, barely heard words of comfort.

Helen had no idea how long she stayed like that in his arms, crying out all her fear and pain and humiliation. All she knew was that it felt good to feel his strong body so close, to feel his hands firm yet strangely soothing as they smoothed over her dishevelled hair, to hear the throbbing depth of his voice rumbling in her ear. When she finally drew away from him he studied her in silence, then gently smoothed the pads of his thumbs under her eyes to wipe away the last of her tears in a gesture which seemed strangely gentle for a man like Jacob.

'All right now?'

There was something in his voice which made a shudder race through her, and Helen drew further away from him, suddenly afraid. The Jacob Hunt she was used to she could handle, but this man, this tender, gentle stranger was outside her experience.

'Yes. I—I'm fine now. Thank you.' She sounded stilted to her own ears and to Jacob's, she didn't doubt, and hurried on. 'What happened before, Jacob—it was all just a misunderstanding, I'm sure.'

'A misunderstanding?' He stiffened at once, all traces of tenderness fading so abruptly that Helen wondered if she must have imagined them. 'There was no misunderstanding, Helen. If I hadn't arrived when I did, then I leave you to imagine what might have happened!'

Her face flamed at his bluntness but she faced him proudly. 'Richard was upset. Normally he wouldn't dream of acting the way he did just now. I'm not making excuses for him but I can understand the strain he must have been under recently.'

'And that's why he came here and virtually assaulted you?' Jacob laughed harshly, his eyes blazing so that Helen took an instinctive step back. 'But of course it's all understandable in the circumstances. Normally, Richard would never do such a thing. He's too much of a gentleman for that!'

His sarcasm stung, and she glared back at him. 'Richard was hurt, and no wonder. Perhaps it's difficult for you to appreciate the kind of anguish he has been going through, Jacob!'

He seemed to tower over her, his body rigid. 'Yes, it is difficult, my sweet. Difficult to understand why you are prepared to excuse behaviour which is totally inexcusable. But then we are talking about Richard, aren't

we? And you know exactly what *he* is like the same as
you know exactly what *I* am like. And nothing will ever
change your views!'

He turned on his heel and strode towards the door,
yet suddenly Helen knew that she couldn't let him leave
like this. There had been something in his voice just now
which had sounded almost like pain, but that was ridiculous. Jacob was invulnerable. No one could ever hurt
him! Yet the sheer craziness of the thought drove her to
call him back.

'Wait! Jacob—please.'

He paused and glanced back, his face betraying little
as he stared at her. 'What now?' He smiled suddenly in
a way which made her heart turn over at the savagery
of it. 'But of course, Helen. Are you worried that I might
do the sensible thing and inform Richard that he no
longer has a job with my company? Were you going to
plead with me to be lenient with him?' He laughed
deeply. 'Don't worry, darling. Every dog is allowed one
bite after all, and that was Richard's.'

Helen flushed, searching his face for any sign of what
she'd thought she might see, but there was nothing and
she experienced a strange disappointment she couldn't
explain and didn't enjoy. It made her reply far more tartly
than she'd intended to. 'No. I wouldn't waste my breath
doing that, Jacob. You're impervious to pleas of any
kind. I shall just put my faith in that contract we signed
today.'

Jacob smiled tightly, feeling in his jacket pocket to
pull out a long manila envelope. 'And that's why I came
back here.' He tossed the envelope on to the desk. 'It's
your copy of our agreement, Helen. You left it behind
in the car, so I thought I had better bring it round for

you to put in a safe place. Good job I did, eh? Still, at least you know where you stand with me.'

He left without another word or backward glance, closing the door quietly behind him. Helen went to the desk and picked up the envelope, holding it between both her hands like a lifeline.

She knew exactly where she stood with Jacob all right, she had known that right from the beginning. So why did it suddenly feel as though the ground had shifted under her feet again? Why, when she thought she knew everything there was to know about him, did there seem to be so many unanswered questions? And why should she even care what they were all of a sudden?

CHAPTER SIX

THERE was a bowl of flowers on the registrar's desk. Their scent filled the air, heavy and cloying, making her feel sick.

Helen lifted a hand to wipe away a bead of perspiration from her upper lip, then stopped when her fingers brushed against the stiffness of the veil on her hat. Her hand dropped to her side, her fingers clenching and unclenching on the fine cream cashmere cloth of her suit. She'd thought that she could go through with this, thought that the burning hatred and desire for revenge would be enough, but now she wasn't certain any longer. How could she marry Jacob and make what must surely be the biggest mistake of her life?

Panic seemed to claw inside her breast and she half turned, then felt Jacob's fingers close around her hand. 'Are you all right, Helen?'

His voice barely carried above the solid drone of the registrar's as he carried on with the wedding service, oblivious to all the undercurrents. Helen drew in a steadying breath then glanced up into Jacob's dark face as she searched for—what? Some sign that he felt as uneasy as she did about what they were doing? But there was nothing in his blue eyes or on that strongly carved face which even hinted at uncertainty. Jacob had made his plans and carried them through, one by one, and now she had to be just as determined as he in order to make him pay for every single thing he had done!

84

When the registrar asked for her responses she gave them in a steady voice, staring straight into Jacob's eyes so that he could see the hatred and contempt she felt for him. Yet when it came to his turn to repeat the words of commitment Helen felt a shudder run through her. Jacob sounded as though he meant the words he spoke in that deep, steady voice, meant this marriage to be real and lasting.

Her pulse leapt, beating wildly under the strong fingers encircling her wrist, and she knew at once that he had felt it. She wanted to snatch her hand away to stop him feeling the betraying sign of weakness, but that would have been even more of a betrayal in a way. The one thing she must never let Jacob start to think was that he could affect her in any way physically. Something warned her that would be far too dangerous.

When the registrar gave permission for Jacob to kiss the bride, Helen steeled herself, but he did no more than brush her mouth with his before he drew away and turned to smile at the few people who had been invited to the ceremony. Apart from her father, Helen hadn't wanted anyone to be there and Jacob had taken her at her word, so that she knew no one else in the party apart from a woman in her late fifties who seemed vaguely familiar. Even as she watched, the woman hurried forwards, smiling as she hugged Jacob and kissed his cheek, then turned to Helen.

'I don't think you really remember me, do you, dear?' At Helen's shake of her head, the woman laughed and patted her arm. 'No, I realised that you didn't when you walked past me before. I'm Jacob's mother.'

Helen stared at the older woman in astonishment, trying hard to reconcile the mental picture she had from

years before with the elegant stranger. Margaret Hunt
had kept very much to herself when she had lived in the
village, but Helen could only ever remember seeing her
simply dressed in chainstore clothes which bore little re-
semblance to the couture outfit she was wearing now.
With her silver-streaked dark hair drawn on top of her
head in an elegant coil, the woman looked far different
from how Helen remembered and she found it hard to
hide her astonishment, but Jacob's mother didn't seem
at all perturbed.

'I know. I'm not at all like you remember, mainly because of all these beautiful clothes Jacob insists on
buying for me.' She turned to smile lovingly at her son,
pride shining in the blue eyes which were so like Jacob's
before she turned back to Helen. 'I just want to wish
you both every happiness. I never thought the day would
come when Jacob's dearest wish would come true. When
he rang to tell me that you had agreed to marry him—
well!' She bent forward and kissed Helen's cheek. 'I'm
sure I don't need to tell you what a wonderful husband
he will make you, Helen. I'm sure you know all his good
points.'

Helen's face flamed, her voice drying up so that she
was unable to find anything to say apart from a meaningless murmur which seemed to be enough. When
Margaret Hunt moved away to speak to one of the few
guests, she glanced up at Jacob and went cold at the
cynical light in his eyes.

'You must forgive my mother, Helen. Obviously she
sees me in a very different light from yours.' Jacob took
her arm, steering her through the guests towards the
door, pausing several times to accept the congratulations showered upon them. Helen said nothing, afraid

that anything she did say might be wrong. Didn't these people know what Jacob was really like? Apparently not, because there was genuine warmth in the smiles they gave him, sincerity in the oft-repeated phrases. It was only when they drew level with her father that Helen dared to speak.

'Father, are you all right? Not getting too tired, I hope?'

Edward Sinclair smiled. 'How can attending my own daughter's wedding be tiring? I'm just so delighted to see you settled at last, darling.' He bent forward to kiss Helen's cheek, then turned to Jacob and held his hand out, 'Just promise me that you will always look after her, Jacob. She is very precious to me.'

Jacob took the elderly man's hand and shook it, his gaze dropping to Helen standing silently beside him. 'That won't be a difficult promise to keep. She's very precious to me also.'

His eyes held Helen's as he spoke the words in a voice which held a note that made the blood suddenly rush to her head. Helen stared back at him, unable to look away from the brilliant blue gaze, then drew a shuddery little breath as she slowly dropped her eyes and called herself every kind of a fool. Of course she was 'precious' to Jacob; he had gone to extraordinary lengths to manoeuvre her into this sham of a marriage! Yet for one crazy moment just now she had almost wished he had meant something very different—but why? Why should she want Jacob to feel anything for her? It didn't make any kind of sense!

'Ladies and gentlemen, I'm sorry to hurry you but there is another party waiting to be married. If you would all please move out into the hallway.' The registrar

bustled about, chivvying everyone out before nodding
to the young couple waiting outside. Helen watched them
go into the room, their faces alight with love as they
glanced at each other. It just served to emphasise what
a mockery her marriage to Jacob was. They were
husband and wife now, supposedly starting out on a new
life together, but what sort of a life would it be based
on beginnings like these?

The thought lingered all through the elegant lunch
Jacob had arranged at one of London's top restaurants.
Helen responded automatically to the attempts to draw
her into the conversation. It was only when Jacob
touched her hand and spoke quietly in her ear that she
shrugged the unease aside, only to find it replaced with
another.

'I think we had better leave now, Helen. We don't
want to be late.' Jacob took her arm and helped her from
the table, leading her quickly out of the restaurant to
where he had left his car. He stopped on the pavement,
his fingers fastening around hers as though he feared
some sort of resistance from her as he turned to reply
to some laughing remark one of the wedding party made.

Helen barely heard what was said, her body a mass
of nerves as she watched Jacob unlock the car door to
urge her to get in. She stood still, staring up at him with
wide eyes.

'Go where? What are we going to be late for?'

'Our flight.' He smiled as he held the door wider. 'Isn't
it traditional for the groom to keep the honeymoon des-
tination a secret as a surprise? But now I can tell you
that we are catching a flight to Nassau in—oh——' he
glanced at his watch then looked back at her '—ap-
proximately one hour's time.'

'Honeymoon!' Her voice rose and she bit her lip. Jacob had made no mention of any honeymoon. If he had, then she would have told him in no uncertain terms that she had no intention of going on one!

'Of course. It's what most newly married couples do, my sweet—take a holiday together before they settle down to the humdrum of everyday life.'

He was mocking her, yet even knowing it couldn't stop her from snapping back, 'We are not most couples, Jacob! Just as this marriage isn't like most marriages. So let me make this clear that I am *not* going on any——'

'Helen? There's nothing wrong is there, darling?' Edward Sinclair's concern was evident as he came up to them. Helen bit back a groan, wishing that her father were a million miles away right then. The last thing she wanted was for him to start worrying again.

'Of course not. Jacob and I were just—just sorting something out,' she finished lamely.

'What?' The elderly man glanced round at the group of guests waiting to wave them off. 'For a moment there I could have sworn you and Jacob were quarrelling, but I hope you weren't, not on your wedding-day?'

Jacob laughed, totally at ease, it seemed. Did nothing ever throw him? Helen thought bitterly, then forgot the rest of the thought when she heard what he said.

'I'm afraid we were, Edward. Well, perhaps not exactly quarrelling, eh, darling? More discussing a point.' He slid his arm around Helen's shoulders and drew her to him, pressing a kiss to her temple. Helen gave him a malevolent stare, but he merely raised a mocking brow as his arm fastened a shade tighter around her, drawing her closer against the hard warmth of his body in a gesture which must have looked loving to anyone watching.

Edward Sinclair laughed softly, not missing the small gesture. 'I know exactly how Helen *discusses* things, so you have my heartfelt sympathy.'

'Father!' Helen stared at her father in part annoyance and part surprise, and heard him chuckle.

'Darling, I've known you all your life and I know just how pig-headed you can be when you get an idea into your head. It's all credit to Jacob that he can be so diplomatic about it. Now tell me what the problem is and let me see if I can help.'

'Well, I...' Her head was reeling from the double on-slaught. That her father should side with Jacob against her...

'The problem is you, I'm afraid, sir.' Jacob's voice was bland, belying the increasing pressure of his fingers on her shoulder, a silent warning that Helen wasn't to disagree with him.

'Me? I'm afraid I don't understand.' There was a stiff note in the elderly man's voice now and Jacob smiled, not slow to notice it.

'I was just telling Helen about our honeymoon. I've kept it for a surprise up until now, but perhaps I shouldn't have done.' Jacob shrugged faintly. 'However, what I haven't yet had time to tell her is that you will be well cared for while we are away.' He turned to Helen and smiled tenderly at her in a way which made her temper rise at once by being so blantantly false. 'You see, darling, I realised how worried you would be about your father, so I have arranged for him to stay at the house while we are away.'

'So that's what it is all about?' Edward Sinclair shook his head. 'I'm sorry, Helen, but Jacob did swear me to secrecy. He wanted your honeymoon to be a surprise, you see. But you mustn't worry about me because I shall be fine. Baxter will take good care of me. In fact, I'm really looking forward to it. So off you go, and don't give another thought to how I am.' He patted Helen's arm, obviously relieved that the problem had been resolved so easily.

Helen took a deep breath and counted to ten, but it did little to cool her temper. Once again, Jacob had covered every eventuality, made his plans and carefully set them in motion. But if he imagined that he could continue to manoeuvre her in the direction he chose, he could think again!

Without a word she got into a car, waiting silently while Jacob walked around to climb behind the wheel. He cast her an amused glance, his mouth quirking slightly at the mutinous set of her face. 'Smile, Helen. We don't want people thinking that you aren't looking forward to our new life together, do we?'

Helen pinned an artificially bright smile to her lips and waved to the group, then let the smile fade abruptly the very instant they were out of sight. She turned to Jacob, her eyes stormy, her pale skin faintly flushed. 'You think you're so clever, don't you, Jacob Hunt? You think you can push people into always doing what you want!'

'What's the problem, Helen? Why should it make a difference where we spend the first few weeks of our married life?' He smiled as he turned the car down a side street, slowing as he eased between the double rows of parked cars. 'London or the Bahamas—it makes no difference to how you feel about me, surely?'

'Of course not! Wherever we are I shall still hate you, Jacob!'

He shrugged faintly, stopping as the traffic lights turned red, then cast her a slow glance which held a certain watchfulness. 'Then why are you so upset about the thought of this honeymoon?' He laughed softly, the sound rippling around the car, dark and strangely disturbing. It seemed to run along her nerves, making her whole body throb in response to the velvet note, setting up a chain reaction of sensations. 'Are you afraid that your hatred might melt a little in the heat of a tropical sun, that it might not be so easy to remember why you dislike me, my sweet?'

'I—no! I've already told you it doesn't matter where we are. It won't change how I feel about you!' Her heart was pounding, her breathing rapid and shallow. It was the sound of that deep laugh, that haunting, evocative quality which awoke memories inside her she'd almost forgotten. It took her back in time to when she had first met Jacob. He had always stayed on the fringes of the group she was friends with, yet whenever he was around she had always been deeply aware of him. He would laugh and her whole body would pulse with it, her heart picking up its beat. She had forgotten how she'd felt and now it shocked her to feel the same crazy reaction.

'Then, as I said, there isn't really a problem.' Jacob slid the car into gear as the lights changed. 'It's all arranged and I am afraid that it's impossible to change my plans now. There's some business I need to attend to while we are there, so this trip will serve a dual purpose.'

'All arranged?' She laughed scornfully. 'And what about the small matter of clothes. What am I expected to wear while we're away on the island?'

Jacob returned the smile with one of his own, his eyes lingering for a moment on the slender curves of her body before he turned his attention back to the road ahead. 'Frankly, darling, it wouldn't matter to me what you wore; the least amount possible, in fact.' He ignored her gasp of outrage as he continued, 'However, I knew that you wouldn't feel quite the same way about it so I had Baxter's wife pack you a case. If there's anything else you need then it will be a simple enough matter to buy it there.'

Helen sank back in the seat, unable to decide which angered her most, that *deliberately* taunting look Jacob had given her just now or his high-handedness in making the arrangements without bothering to consult her first. Yet deep down she was forced to admit that neither of those things was what bothered her most about this unexpected trip. As Jacob had said, it shouldn't have mattered where they spent the first weeks of their married life, but the thought of a honeymoon disturbed her more than she cared to admit by its very suggestion of shared intimacy. That was something that she and Jacob had never discussed and now she wished she'd made her feelings clear. No matter how real Jacob intended this marriage to appear, there were certain aspects that she had no intention of agreeing to. She might have agreed to share Jacob's life for however long it took to pay him back, but she would be damned if she would agree to share his bed!

* * *

After the misty chill of London, Nassau sweltered under a tropical sun.

Helen followed Jacob from the airport to the car which was waiting to collect them, unfastening the top button of her jacket as the heat hit her. She felt stifled in the elegant wool suit in this climate, although back in London it had barely been warm enough. Now as she flicked the button open and ran a hand down her throat she could feel the dampness of her hot skin.

'We'll soon be at the house. I'm sure you will be glad to get changed into something more suitable.' Jacob held the rear door of the car open for her, looking cool and comfortable in his own equally formal clothing. How typical that as usual he should look perfectly at ease!

'If you had given me a little more warning then I could have arranged to change before we flew out here, then I wouldn't be feeling quite so uncomfortable,' she snapped irritably.

Jacob slid his hand under her elbow to help her into the car, his fingers lingering just a moment longer than was strictly necessary. 'And if I had, then wouldn't you have found any number of excuses not to come?' He laughed softly, his eyes filled with amusement. 'Heaven knows you tried your best to think up a few before!'

Helen wrenched her arm away from his hold, sliding into the car before turning to glare at him as he got in beside her. 'I don't like surprises, especially not those thought up for devious purposes.'

'Devious?' He settled back in the seat, spreading his long legs as best he could in the confined space. His knee brushed against hers and Helen drew away at once from the light contact, then inwardly cursed herself for the betraying reaction when she saw his smile deepen in acknowledgement. She looked away, wondering why she always felt so ridiculously aware of Jacob. As a very attractive woman, she had never lacked for male attention, yet Jacob seemed to make all other men pale by comparison. Despite the sophisticated veneer he had acquired through his wealth, there was an innate toughness about him and something inside her responded to it.

'Why should it be devious to want to take my new bride away on honeymoon? What do you imagine I have planned, Helen?'

Helen pushed the strangely disquieting thoughts aside as she stared out of the window as the driver turned the car on to the road heading towards the town. 'I have no idea, but, knowing you, Jacob, there's bound to be something at the back of all this.'

'You really do have a low opinion of me, don't you, sweet? I shall have to try to alter that while we are here.'

There was a note in his deep voice which made alarm skitter through her and she shot him a wary glance. He arched one dark brow, obviously perfectly aware of how she felt. Helen flushed, her eyes warring with his before she turned back to the window, barely noticing the small houses they were passing, washed in pastel tones of pink and green. She must be more careful what she said, must try to keep a rein on her tongue. The last thing she wanted was for Jacob to start thinking she was issuing challenges to him!

'To set your mind at rest, Helen, I have nothing planned other than a holiday where we can hopefully get to know each other better.'

'Better?' She turned to smile at him, all thoughts of caution forgotten in the face of that bland yet totally ridiculous statement. 'I don't think that's possible, Jacob. I imagine I know you better than an awful lot of people do—know the *real* you that is not that charming mask you hide behind so well!'

'And it has never occurred to you that it might be you who are mistaken about me, Helen? That other people see me for what I am while you see me through eyes tainted with bitterness?'

'No. I'm not mistaken. I better than anyone know what you're capable of, Jacob.'

'Do you?' He sighed as he leant back against the seat, his face suddenly weary. 'I wonder how you formed those views, Helen. Were they all yours, or did someone else plant the idea in your head and you merely nurtured it?'

'I have no idea what you mean. Who could possibly have planted anything in my head?' She stared at him in open confusion, and saw him grimace.

'Your mother. You said once that you had known me for years, yet that wasn't quite true, was it? I was seventeen when we first met and just twenty when I left the village. And in between your mother made sure that I knew my place and didn't get too familiar with you. Do you remember that time I called round with your bag, Helen?' He laughed harshly. 'I'm sure you must!'

Helen flushed, remembering all too clearly what he was referring to. She had called in at the library on her way home one day and left her bag behind. Jacob had found it and taken it round to her house to return it to her. It had been Baxter's day off and her mother had answered the door to him herself. Patricia Sinclair had spoken to him with undisguised contempt, not deigning to ask him inside but leaving him standing outside on the step.

Helen could still recall her embarrassment when her mother had called up the stairs to tell her that Jacob was there, not bothering to lower her voice as she had curtly ordered Helen to get rid of him at once as she didn't want the likes of Jacob Hunt around.

Jacob had handed Helen her bag without a word, his expression freezing her halting attempts at an apology. He had left the village shortly after that, returning infrequently to visit his mother until she too had moved, although surprisingly Jacob had bought the small cottage where they had both lived, using it for odd weekends.

'My—my mother had very set views about things, Jacob. Perhaps she was a bit abrupt that day.'

'Not to mention all the other days.' He must have seen her start of surprise because he laughed. 'That wasn't the first time I called around to speak to you, Helen. I had called before but always met with a totally negative response, the same as every time I telephoned you.'

'You telephoned me? But...' She broke off, watching the cynical tilt of his mouth as he looked back at her.

'Now I suppose you're going to claim that you had no idea that I'd ever phoned, that no one ever told you about the messages I left?'

'But I didn't.' Without realising what she was doing, Helen laid her hand on his arm, her eyes enormous with shock. 'If you ever left a message for me then I never got it, Jacob. Believe me!'

He glanced down at her hand then slowly caught it with his own, smoothing his thumb over the delicate length of her fingers. 'I am almost tempted to believe you, Helen. Heaven knows, I tried to convince myself enough times all those years ago that was the case!'

The soft touch of his fingers against her skin was starting to affect her, making her blood quicken in her veins, her pulse beat faster and faster as though in a race. There was danger in that touch, danger and a strange heady excitement which scared her. This was Jacob she was dealing with and she must never forget what he was like, how easily he would use any sign of weakness to his advantage.

She drew her hand away from his, forcing herself not to betray any sign of the effect he had on her. 'Whether you believe me or not is up to you.' She affected a shrug. 'Obviously there must have been some sort of misunderstanding and that's why the messages were never passed on. I can only apologise for it.'

His laughter grated, rubbing her already stretched nerves rawly sensitive. 'Spoken like your mother's daughter, Helen. She would have been proud of you, I'm sure, although I don't know what she would feel about this marriage of ours.'

'I imagine she would be perfectly happy once she understood the real reason for it!' Helen couldn't keep the bite out of her voice and she turned her head away at once, afraid of saying more than was wise. What Jacob had just told her shocked her because she'd had no idea at all about what had gone on. What sort of messages had he left for her? And why had Patricia Sinclair gone to such lengths to stop her receiving them?

The puzzle kept her busy during the rest of the drive to the house. Helen shook herself out of her reverie, watching curiously as the car pulled up in front of a creamy pink wall behind which she could just make out the green-tiled roof of a long, low bungalow.

Jacob got out of the car, paying the driver before helping the man unload their cases from the boot. With a wide smile and a friendly wave the man drove off, and Jacob picked up the bags, nodding to Helen to open the gate set into the wall while he carried them through into a garden which was a riot of colour. Helen paused to look round, her gaze lingering appreciatively on the brilliantly coloured flowers which spilled from huge terracotta pots, making a startling contrast to the pale pink walls of the house with its white-painted louvred shutters.

'It's lovely, Jacob,' she said involuntarily. 'I never imagined it would be like this.'

'Why? What did you expect? Something ultra-modern in steel and glass, all rather flashy?' He set the cases down as he closed the gate, his face set into hard lines, and Helen sighed.

'No, I didn't. You have far better taste than that. I just meant that I never expected so much colour. It comes as quite a shock after London's drabness.'

Jacob's expression softened. 'It's one of the things I like best about this place; all year round there's such richness of colour. I've never regretted my decision to buy the house even though the amount of time I can spend here is, by necessity, limited.'

He took a key out of his pocket and unlocked the white-painted door, pushing it wide so that Helen could enter the house. With the shutters drawn the interior was cool and shadowy, yet there was the fragrance of fresh flowers and polish, as though the house had recently been cleaned.

Jacob carried the cases inside then set them down as he walked across the hall and pushed the shutters back to allow light to spill inside across the smooth polished wood floor. The entrance hall led directly into a huge lounge area and Helen walked into it, looking around curiously at the elegant yet comfortable furniture covered in creamy-toned fabric and piled with heaps of brilliantly coloured cushions. There were water-colours on the walls, scenes of Bahamian life mixed with several seascapes. She crossed the room to study one which caught her eye, admiring the expert brushwork, the delicate blending of tones.

'Like it?' Jacob walked over to join her, watching her quietly, yet Helen could sense a certain tenseness about him. She frowned slightly as she turned to look at the picture again, wondering what had caused it, then gasped when she suddenly noticed the signature at the bottom right hand corner of the painting. She turned back to him with shock glittering in her eyes.

'You painted this?'

'Mmm. I do quite a bit of painting when I'm here. I find it relaxing.'

She had no idea why she should feel so shocked, but she was. Her eyes lingered for a moment more on the painting before she turned away from it almost abruptly, but suddenly Jacob was there in front of her, stopping her from moving away.

'Something new you didn't know about me, Helen? I told you you might be in for a few surprises.'

His voice sounded even deeper than usual, soft and vibrant, and she shivered in an uncontrollable reaction to it. Just for a moment her eyes lifted to his and she went hot at the expression which showed so briefly in their depths before he gave a low, taunting laugh which broke the spell at once. 'Are you still so confident that you won't need to change your views of me, darling?'

Helen drew in a shaky breath, fighting to control the pounding beat of her heart as she stared up into his mocking face. 'It will take more than this to make me change my mind about you, Jacob! Now if you don't mind I would like to get showered and changed.' She gave him a challenging little smile. 'I'm sure there will be plenty of time later for me to make suitably admiring remarks about your new-found talent.'

If he was annoyed by her sarcasm he gave no sign. He merely stepped aside for her to pass him and smiled in a way which made her palm itch to come into contact with his mocking face. 'Of course. You're absolutely right, Helen. For the next couple of weeks we shall have all the time in the world to make fresh discoveries about each other. I can hardly wait.'

Her face flamed at the deliberately taunting statement, but she faced him squarely. 'And I think it's time we got a few ground rules established.'

'Oh, I'm sure I already know what they are.' He picked up her case and crossed the hall, opening a door. Through it Helen could see that it was a bedroom, done in the same cool and airy style as the lounge area. In a fast sweep her eyes took stock of the elegant, expensive furnishings then came to a sudden halt on the huge double bed with its canopy of white broderie anglaise. Suddenly it felt as though some unseen hand had gripped her, stopping the air mid-way to her lungs, and she had to fight for breath before she could attempt to speak in a reedy little voice. 'Look, Jacob, I . . .'

'What, Helen? Want to make it clear that you have no intention of sharing a bedroom with me?' He paused as he watched the hot colour flood her pale face, then turned to carry her case into the room and set it down on the bottom of the bed before glancing back at her with a sardonic lift of his brows. 'I already anticipated that. This is your room. I shall be using the one across the hall. Now I shall leave you to get settled in.'

He walked past her, disappearing through a door on the opposite side and closing it behind him with a soft finality which made her want to scream. She curbed the urge. Slowly she walked into the bedroom and looked round, studying the tasteful blend of furniture and fabrics while she gave herself time to regain her control, but it was difficult.

Once again Jacob had out-manoeuvred her, and it wasn't pleasant realising he could read her so easily. At every turn he seemed to be a few steps ahead, making his plans and carrying them through with an almost galling ease. Yet somehow she had to make her own plans, plans which would eventually bring about his downfall. She could never rest until she had made Jacob pay for all he had done!

CHAPTER SEVEN

HELEN didn't mean to fall asleep. After she had showered and slipped on a lightweight robe she lay down on the bed to rest for a while, only to wake some time later to darkness.

For a moment she lay still, trying to orientate herself in the strange room, then slowly the memory of where she was surfaced. She swung her legs off the bed and walked over to the window, surprised to find the French doors open. She didn't recall opening them but she must have done.

There was a deliciously cool breeze blowing in through the opening and on a sudden impulse she pushed the doors wide and walked out on to the veranda which ran along the side of the bungalow. Walking over to the rail which marked the edge of it, she stared across the white sand towards the sea which glittered under a full moon. It was almost idyllically peaceful, just the soft rhythmic sound of the ocean vying gently with the rustling of the palm trees stirred by the breeze, and she sighed softly in appreciation.

'How do you feel now? Less tired after your sleep?'

She gasped at the unexpected sound of that deep voice, swinging round to pinpoint where Jacob was. Her eyes searched the shadows by the house then came to a halt when she found him seated in a chair further along the veranda. Even as she watched he got up and came towards her, stopping several feet away as he studied her with a thoroughness which brought the colour into her face. She turned away at once to go back inside, suddenly achingly conscious of her state of near undress, the thinness of the robe which the breeze was plastering against her body, and heard Jacob exclaim almost wearily.

'For heaven's sake, Helen, I won't bite! You don't need to go rushing off as though I terrify you.'

She stopped uncertainly, drawn to a halt by that note in his voice and her own realisation of how foolishly she was acting. 'You don't terrify me, Jacob. Don't flatter yourself.'

He laughed shortly. 'No? Then you give a very good impression of it.'

'I was merely going inside to get dressed,' she said stiffly, then wished she'd held her tongue when she felt his gaze drop to the slender curves of her body, clearly outlined through the soft clinging cotton. The feel of his gaze made her go hot all over yet surprisingly, when he replied, there was no hint of anything, not even that mockery she had come to expect, in his tone.

'You're wearing far more than you would on the beach so don't worry about it. Come and have a glass of wine, Helen, and relax for a while.' When she continued to hesitate he smiled faintly. 'I'm sure we are both adult enough to call a truce for a while, aren't we, without it endangering the outcome of the war?'

He walked back along the veranda and sat down again, leaving Helen to follow or not as she chose. For a moment she stood undecided, wondering if it was wise, then with a shrug followed him and sat down on one of the comfortable wicker chairs arranged beside a small cane table. There would undoubtedly be many battles to fight in the future, she didn't doubt, so why waste her strength when there appeared to be no need?

When Jacob poured her a glass of wine, she accepted it with a nod of thanks and took a sip, letting the cool liquid rest on her tongue for a second before swallowing it gratefully. She hadn't realised before just how thirsty she was, and the wine tasted good, fresh and clean as it trickled down her dry throat.

'There's food if you're hungry.' Jacob pushed a platter of cold meats and salad across the table towards her, then set a basket of small fresh rolls beside it. 'Nothing fancy, I'm afraid, but everything is fresh.'

Helen glanced at the tempting array, suddenly realising that she was hungry as well as thirsty. She had refused everything apart from coffee on the flight, too tense and strung up to eat the meal offered; now her stomach was telling her that it was way past time she had something. Taking one of the plates, she selected several slices of meat and a generous helping of salad, then broke one of the small rolls open and buttered it. It tasted delicious, light and airy, almost melting in her mouth.

Jacob must have seen her appreciation because he sat back in his chair, watching her almost indulgently as she ate. 'I thought you would want something when you woke up. It must be hours since you last ate, Helen.'

The way he was watching her made her feel self-conscious although she couldn't explain why. Hurriedly Helen finished the light meal and popped the final piece of roll into her mouth, then visibly jumped when he suddenly leaned towards her. Her eyes flew to meet his, wide and startled, and she saw him shake his head as he caught her chin and turned her face towards the dim light spilling from the house on to the veranda.

'Relax. You've got a smear of butter on your lip. I'm only going to wipe it away so don't panic.'

He picked up a napkin, wiped it over the corner of her upper lip and dropped it back on to the table, yet even then he didn't release her. Instead his hand slid down her throat, his fingers coming to rest on the pulse which was beating a tattoo at the base of it, betraying her agitation so clearly. 'Is it fear that makes your pulse race like this, Helen? Or is it something else?'

His voice was soft in the night's stillness, barely carrying above the swishing sound of the waves, the sighing of the breeze as it rustled the stiff leaves, yet to Helen's ears it seemed unnaturally loud, blanking out all the other sounds. Her head seemed to be full of those rich tones, her body shuddering convulsively as they stroked across her skin. When Jacob gently drew his hand back up her throat and slid his fingers along the curve of her jaw, she stared at him as though mesmerised and heard him give a low, harsh exclamation which seemed to be torn from him. 'Helen!'

There was so much emotion in that single word that it shocked her. This was Jacob, tough, ruthless Jacob, yet when he said her name that way there was something oddly vulnerable about the sound of it, as though for a moment he had almost lost that formidable control he always held over himself.

Suddenly Helen felt afraid, afraid that she was crossing some unseen line beyond which she would be incapable of controlling her own destiny. She tried to free herself from his hold, her eyes luminously green in the glow from the moon. 'Jacob, I don't think...'

'The trouble is that you *think* far too much, Helen. You always have.' His fingers curved around the back of her head, warm and firm, holding her when she would have moved out of his grasp, drawing her imperceptibly closer to him. 'Just for a few minutes, sweet, don't think...just feel.'

He drew her to him, bending as she came closer to fit his mouth to hers in a long drugging kiss which left her feeling so shaken that she couldn't stop the helpless gasp which left her lips. Jacob stiffened when he heard that betraying little sound, his eyes staring straight into hers from the distance of mere inches until Helen felt that she was drowning in the glittering blue depths, drowning in the emotion she could see swirling in them. She closed her eyes against the devastating sight but that was a mistake, because now her other senses took control. She could smell the musky, heady scent of his skin, feel the warmth of his body, hear the rapid sound of his breathing mingling with her own, taste the coolness of the wine on his lips, and she was suddenly lost in a maelstrom of feelings and emotions.

When Jacob pulled her even closer to him to deepen the kiss she made no attempt to stop him, her hands sliding up the warm hard muscles of his chest to rest against his shoulders. Under her hands his skin seemed to burn, the heat so intense that it spread from him to her, heating her own blood to a degree whereby it seemed to scorch her veins, filling her with fire which burned away any lingering thoughts of resisting.

Her mouth opened willingly under his seeking lips, her whole body shuddering as she felt his tongue slide inside to tangle with hers in a heady rhythm which stirred her unbearably. It was like nothing she had ever felt before, this hot, wild turbulence of emotions. It was rawly elemental, demanding her response, allowing her no leeway. Jacob kissed her and she kissed him back just as deeply, just as desperately, because at that moment that was the thing she wanted to do most in the world.

When he started to draw back away from her, she whimpered softly, her hands clinging to him convulsively, but all he did was stand up and draw her with him, obviously impatient with the restrictions their seated positions imposed upon the closeness of their bodies. His hands slid down her spine, moulding her to him, so close that she could feel every hard muscle imprinted against her softness, feel the heavy, rapid rising and falling of his powerful chest, the pressure of his thighs. And all the while he kissed her, his mouth demanding more and more from her, more than she had thought herself capable of giving, more than she had given to any man before.

'Jacob!' Was that really her voice sounding so full of longing and excitement as it said his name in the silence? Helen knew it must be yet she seemed oddly divorced from it, as though she listened to the voice of a stranger, but then she was acting like a stranger now. She had never felt this way before, never felt the blood pulsing in her veins, never felt the burning heat of desire.

He drew back abruptly, his eyes glittering as he stared down at her. 'I knew this would be how it could be, Helen. And I was right!'

There was undisguised triumph in his voice now, mingling with the throbbing note of passion, and she went cold. She stared up at him with wide, shocked eyes, suddenly realising what she was doing and what she had been inviting! How could she have been such a fool as to let this happen?

Shame was just as cold as passion had been hot. It filled every part of her, making her want to run from her own foolishness, but pride dictated that she should try to hide how she felt from Jacob.

'Were you? Do you really imagine that I could forget all you have done so easily?' She laughed scornfully, praying that he wouldn't hear the real truth behind the brave words. 'Please let me go.'

He released her at once, his face betraying little as he watched her. Helen smoothed a hand over her dishevelled hair, avoiding his eyes as she tried to regain her shattered composure.

'Are you saying that this was all a calculated act designed to trick me in some way?'

'Of course. You don't really imagine that I enjoyed having you kiss me, do you, Jacob?' She gave a small forced laugh, then shrank back when he took a slow step towards her.

'Oh, I'd say that you gave a good impression of doing just that, darling.' He reached out suddenly to catch her arm and draw her to him, smiling faintly as he ran his thumb across the swollen fullness of her mouth. 'A *very* good impression, in fact.'

Helen tried to push his hand away from her mouth but Jacob merely captured her hands in his and held them behind her back, curving her closer against the hard strength of his body while he smiled down into her angry face. 'You wanted my kisses just now, Helen. You wanted anything and everything I was prepared to offer you and we both know that, the same as we both know it's just a matter of time before we repeat that very enjoyable experience.' His fingers took another lazy, sensuously disturbing journey across her mouth before he let her go and turned to walk away.

Helen drew herself up, hating him for his arrogance, for the fact that he *knew* how she had felt. 'There won't be any repeat, Jacob. I won't let you get close enough for that!'

He stopped to look back, big and indolently at ease, his dark hair falling rakishly across his brow, his mouth slightly swollen as hers must be from those long, drugging kisses. 'I'm prepared to wait to disprove that, Helen, for however long it takes.' He shrugged lightly. 'I have waited a long time already so it won't worry me. But one day in the not too distant future you will admit that you want me and what I can offer you.'

'Never! Never, Jacob!' She shouted the denial aloud but he didn't bother answering as he disappeared inside the house. Helen sat down abruptly on the chair, clenching her hands against a sudden wild panic. He was wrong! She didn't want him and never would. What had just happened had been some sort of fluke. She was tired, her nerves stretched to their limits with all the strain she'd been under recently, and Jacob was experienced with women; he knew how to draw a response from them. But now she knew how dangerous he could be she would never make the mistake of allowing him to get so close again!

The sun was an orange ball in a cloudless blue sky. Helen adjusted the back of the sun-lounger as she sat up to rub more sunscreen into her skin. In the three days since they had arrived in Nassau the weather seemed to have got hotter and hotter. Even Rita-May, the local woman Jacob employed on a daily basis to clean and shop, had

admitted that the heat was starting to affect her too that
morning.

'You need to take care, Helen. Don't stay out in this
sun too long. It would be foolish with your skin.'

Helen glanced round at the sound of that familiar deep
voice, feeling her heart giving that strange little leap it
had started doing each time Jacob appeared recently.
Was it just nerves causing this strange reaction? She imagined so, and with just cause.

Although they had maintained a civilised veneer of
harmony during the past three days as they had swum
and sailed the small yacht Jacob kept moored off shore
close to the bungalow, Helen had the feeling that it had
been merely a brief cessation of hostilities in the battle
they were waging. That first night lay between them, not
forgotten but merely pushed to the background for now
until Jacob chose to mention it again. He had developed
a way of watching her which told her he was biding his
time, confident that what he had predicted would come
true, and although she told herself that the dangers of
her making such a mistake again were negligible, it still
made her feel on edge and far more aware of him than
she wanted to be.

Now she forced a note of indifference to her voice,
refusing to let him guess how she felt. 'Don't worry,
Jacob. I'm well able to look after myself without you
having to concern yourself about me.'

He stepped down off the veranda and came across the
sand to where she was lying on the lounger, stopping
just a few feet away as he subjected her to an intent
scrutiny which made her shift self-consciously on the
cushions. In a slow, deliberately thorough sweep, his eyes
traced the curves of her slender body in the clinging one-

piece black costume before coming back to rest on her face.

Helen tried to hold his gaze, her face colouring when she saw the light in his blue eyes. Silently but clearly Jacob was letting her know that he enjoyed looking at her in the revealing outfit and Helen wasn't proof against that no matter how hard she tried!

'I am your husband, Helen, so naturally I'm concerned about your welfare.'

She glared up at him as she drew the lightweight wrap around her. 'How touching! I could almost believe you mean that!'

'Of course I mean it. My main concern for some time now has been your well-being, Helen.'

His words sparked her anger. 'Your main concern has been getting what you want, Jacob! And it made no difference who suffered so long as you achieved that.'

His face darkened as he came the last few feet to stand towering over where she was lying. In contrast to how Helen was dressed he was wearing an elegant lightweight suit in an expensive pale grey fabric with a white shirt and a grey and burgundy silk tie, and he looked every inch the tough, ruthless business tycoon as he stood there and stared down at her so coldly.

'You have never suffered at my hand, Helen. Let's get that straight.'

'No? Then what do you call the loss of my family's business and home? Do you imagine it was pleasant watching my father making himself ill going through the agony of that, Jacob? And it was all your doing.'

He sat down abruptly on the lounger, trapping her with his body so that she couldn't get away. 'I had nothing whatsoever to do with any of it, Helen. Nothing!'

'How can you say that? You drove my father to near bankruptcy because you wanted to take away everything we had, punish us for the ''wrongs'' we had done you!'

He stopped her when she tried to wriggle away, his fingers biting into the soft flesh of her upper arms as he held her, while he stared into her angry face with an anger equal to if not greater than her own. 'Is that what your father told you? Well?' He shook her hard, sending the heavy weight of red hair spilling from beneath the straw sun hat she was wearing. It tumbled over her shoulders, a fiery contrast to her ivory skin, but Helen made no attempt to push it back, too caught up with the moment and what Jacob was saying.

'No one told me anything, Jacob,' she spat venomously back. 'No one needed to. I added it all up for myself and worked out what had gone on!'

'Did you, indeed?' He laughed harshly in a way which made the hair on the back of Helen's neck rise. Suddenly she felt afraid of the anger she had aroused in him, afraid of what other emotions it might unleash as well.

'Jacob, I——'

He cut her off as though she hadn't spoken, his fingers holding her so hard that Helen winced from the pressure, yet she knew that he was unaware of it. 'You saw what you wanted to and made the deductions you chose to make because you were biased. What do you imagine I did, Helen? Do you honestly believe that I found some way to drive your family's *thriving* business into the ground? Do you really think that I was so concerned with doing that, to gain possession of some small firm, when I had a multi-million-pound company to run?' He shook his head, a lock of dark hair falling over his forehead, black and glittering in the hot sun. His skin had been tanned when they had arrived in Nassau and with the heat of the past few days his tan had deepened to a mahogany hue. He looked almost savage sitting there with those brilliant blue eyes glittering, his hard-boned face set. It wasn't difficult to imagine Jacob in the guise of one of the pirates who centuries before had made the Bahamas their hunting ground. Even in that sort of rough company Jacob could have held his own and come out on top, Helen suddenly thought. It wasn't a comforting realisation.

'Grow up, Helen. See things for what they really are, not what you try to make them.'

She shook the disquieting thoughts aside. 'Meaning what?'

'Simply that the fact is that your father was on the verge of placing the business into the hands of the receiver when he approached me to see if I would help.'

The flat statement almost took her breath away. 'What? Did you really say what I think you did?'

Jacob smiled tightly, his expression never softening. 'Yes.'

'And do you really imagine that I would believe such a trumped-up tale?' She tried to inject scorn into her voice, but knew she hadn't been successful when Jacob smiled again with a shade more warmth. It made her feel deeply uneasy, as though he knew things she didn't.

'There's nothing trumped-up about it. The business was on its uppers when I became involved at the request of your father. The bank had already recalled its loan to the firm but there was no way it could be met. The firm had been trading at a substantial loss for several years by then and there was nothing left. Even the mortgage your father raised on the house hadn't been enough to cover a fraction of it.'

'Mortgage? Oh, but—but that can't be right! I had no idea—Father didn't...' She trailed off, watching helplessly as Jacob nodded.

'It's the truth. I imagine your father didn't tell you because he wanted to shield you from the hard facts for as long as he could, but it's all true, Helen. Every word I've told you.'

'But how did the business get in such a state? It used to be a thriving concern, one of the oldest and most respected electrical manufacturing companies in the country. Are you telling me that you had nothing to do with its downfall, that you did nothing to ruin it? I don't believe that!'

'I am. If the business failed it was none of my doing.' He shrugged. 'Lack of foresight, poor management, just plain basic economics were the contributing factors. To keep any firm healthy one always has to be looking ahead for new ideas, a fresh approach to set it ahead of any competition. And you need to trim costs ruthlessly. Your father did none of those things and the consequence was that the company was running at a huge loss for years before I became involved.'

'But why would Father turn to you? It's crazy! There must have been someone else he could have gone to?' Helen hadn't intended that to sound like a deliberate insult but that was how Jacob took it, she knew, as he got up and stared coldly at her.

'I imagine because he knew I was the one person who would take the risk of getting involved. Not many others would have agreed to take on a business which was riddled with debt and tried to retain as many as possible of the staff.'

Because Helen felt somehow guilty at her unwitting slight she took a defensive stand. 'So what you are saying is that you were our salvation rather than the cause of our downfall?' She laughed softly as she gathered the silky waves of hair into a coil and pinned it back on top of her head. 'That's hard to believe!'

Jacob's eyes were hard as blue glass. 'Then I suggest you set your mind to it, Helen. If I hadn't stepped in then your father would have lost the lot *and* been declared bankrupt into the bargain because there was no way that he could cover the massive personal debts he had accrued by then.

'The money I paid for the business and the house plus its contents was just sufficient to clear them although, as you know, there wasn't anything over to keep you both in the manner to which you were accustomed.' He smiled coldly. 'To put it bluntly, sweet, I was the only one prepared to help when you needed it most.'

'But why?' She came to her feet in a rush. 'What motive did you have for such remarkable generosity, Jacob?'

He ignored her sarcasm, merely glancing at his watch before looking back at her flushed face. 'I had my reasons. Several good ones. However, I don't have time to discuss them now. I have an appointment downtown in half an hour's time so you must excuse me.'

He walked back inside the house and after a few minutes Helen heard a car engine and the sound of a car driving off down the road. She sank down on to the lounger and stared blankly out to sea as she went back over everything Jacob had just told her, trying to make sense of it.

Edward Sinclair had approached Jacob and *asked* him to take over control of the business, willingly sold him the house to clear their debts! It added a whole new dimension to what had happened if she could believe it, but why should Jacob lie when she could easily find out the truth? But yet why had he done it? If the firm had been in such a sorry state by then Jacob could have waited and bought it from the receivers rather than paying out the small fortune it must have cost to keep it running. As he'd said, Hunt Electronics had been well established by then, a huge international concern which hadn't needed either the Sinclair name nor its debts. So why had Jacob agreed when her father approached him?

It was all very puzzling and oddly disturbing in a way, as though by finding the answer to it Helen would find the answer to so many other puzzles as well. If she found out what Jacob's reasons had been, then would she also find a way to pay him back? But for what? If Jacob hadn't driven her father to near bankruptcy, what was he guilty of? She had hated him for so long, yet suddenly the basis for all that hatred seemed to be slipping away and Helen felt afraid.

If she couldn't think of Jacob as her enemy, then how should she think of him?

CHAPTER EIGHT

THE day dragged past, morning drifting into afternoon while Helen was barely aware of the time passing. The puzzles seemed to whirl inside her head until it throbbed with them but she could find no answers or solutions. Only Jacob knew why he had done such a thing, yet she wasn't sure she wanted him to explain now. Somehow the answers seemed fraught with danger although she couldn't explain why she should feel that way.

When Rita-May stopped in the lounge before she left, it took an effort for Helen to give her her full attention. 'Did you want me?'

Rita-May looked worriedly towards the window where storm clouds were gathering low on the horizon. 'I was just wondering how long Mr Hunt would be.'

Helen forced a smile; the longer Jacob took, the better as far as she was concerned. It gave her more time to come to terms with what he had told her and decide how to handle it, but of course she couldn't tell Rita-May that. 'I'm not sure. He had some business to attend to. If there's a problem, maybe I can help?'

The woman shook her head, the gold hoop earrings she wore swinging back and forth. 'No problem. I just don't like the look of those clouds. There's a storm coming and you'll be here by yourself once I leave.'

'I'm sure he won't be much longer.' Helen stood up and walked over to the window, only then becoming aware of the mass of dark clouds which had started to blot out the sun. The wind had risen, whirling the sand into drifts along the beach and whipping frothy white-capped waves into shore. Although the bungalow was less than half an hour's drive from downtown Nassau, with its huge banking and commercial centre, it was the only property along this stretch of road. If Jacob didn't get back before the storm broke then she could find herself stranded alone once Rita-May left, but she really couldn't expect the woman to stay with her when she had her own family to see to.

She turned back with a reassuring smile. 'I shall be fine. The storm can't be that bad otherwise there would have been a warning posted.'

Rita-May rolled expressive dark eyes. 'They sure don't always get it right! But if you're sure you don't want me to stay...' She glanced towards the door, obviously eager to be on her way.

'Of course not. Off you go. I hope you make it home before the storm arrives.' Helen followed her into the hall and waved her off before closing the door with a heavy sigh. She glanced at her watch, surprised to see just how late it was. She'd been so caught up in her thoughts that she'd been unaware of the time passing. It was really time she got showered and changed. She wanted to look good tonight, cool and poised. It would give a much needed boost to her confidence. Doubting beliefs she'd held for so long now was unsettling, but until she had a lot more answers then she couldn't risk allowing Jacob to know how she felt!

It took only seconds to strip off her clothes and step into the shower. Helen adjusted the temperature until the water ran coolly over her, sighing in appreciation.

The impending storm had turned the air uncomfortably humid and it was a relief to wash the stickiness away.

Finally refreshed by the lengthy shower, she switched the water off and wrapped a towel around herself to walk back through to the bedroom, then gasped at the scene beyond the bedroom window. The black clouds were almost directly overhead now, filling the room with an odd purplish gloom. Even as she watched, the storm rolled closer, the wind bending the palm trees surrounding the bungalow almost double with its force. When the blast hit the French windows they flew open, sending the curtains billowing crazily so that a small Tiffany lamp on a nearby table fell to the floor and smashed.

Helen ran to the window, carefully avoiding the jagged pieces, and struggled to close it, but it took several attempts to fasten it securely. She caught her breath for a moment. She had never felt wind like that before, so strong that it was an actual physical force which needed to be fought against. It took the sound of glass shattering elsewhere in the house to rouse her to the fact that she must do something to curtail the damage the storm might cause.

Grabbing jeans and T-shirt from the closet, Helen struggled into them then ran from room to room closing windows, but it soon became obvious that the wind would find them a fragile barrier. What she needed to do was close the shutters as further protection.

Opening the door was easy; the wind ripped it out of her hands and sent it crashing against the wall. Helen grimaced as she saw the huge gouge it had made in the plaster but there was little she could do about it. Clutching at whatever handholds she could find, she battled her way outside and was instantly drenched as the heavens opened to send a deluge of water down from the black sky.

Cursing her bad luck and anything else which seemed appropriate, she struggled along the front of the house and tried to latch the shutters across the windows, but it was almost impossible with the wind tearing them out of her hands all the time.

'What the hell are you doing out here?'

When strong hands caught her by the shoulders and a voice boomed in her ear she nearly shot out of her skin. She half turned then staggered back under the force of the wind, and would have fallen if Jacob hadn't steadied her, his eyes dark with anger as he studied her sodden hair and clothing. Helen had no idea what he was annoyed about. After all, it was his property she was trying to secure!

'I should have thought that was obvious. Instead of asking stupid questions, Jacob, why don't you help me get these shut?' She turned back to the task then gave a startled scream when she felt herself being lifted unceremoniously off her feet. When Jacob started marching back towards the front door, which was banging back and forth with the wind, she clutched at his shoulders instinctively to steady herself even while she gasped out a protest.

'Put me down at once! This is ridiculous.'

Jacob bent into the wind, his face close to hers, his eyes slitted against the dirt and debris which were flying around. 'Shut up, Helen. Just for once, do as you're told, will you, without a fuss!'

Not bothering to wait for her reply, he struggled back inside the house then swung her out of his arms, breathing heavily from his exertions. The rain had soaked him too, his jacket darkened with water, the fine white shirt clinging transparently to the strong muscles in his chest as it rose and fell with every laboured breath he took. Helen stared at him, drinking in the sight he made as he stood there, and felt heat surge through her. Helplessly, her gaze lifted to his face but Jacob was already turning to go back outside and missed the shock which showed in her eyes at her unexpected reaction.

'Stay inside and keep away from the windows until I get those shutters fastened. You don't want to risk getting cut if they smash under the force of that wind.'

He was gone in a second, his far superior strength enabling him to work his way along the house closing the shutters. Helen stayed where she was, unaware that she was dripping water on to the highly polished floor. That surge of raw desire she'd felt had knocked her completely off balance. It was only when Jacob finally struggled back through the door that she rallied herself again.

'I—I'd better go and get some dry clothes on.' She turned to go then stopped when Jacob spoke in a strangely gentle tone.

'There's no need to be frightened, Helen. The storm will blow itself out fairly quickly, I imagine.'

Jacob had mistaken one fear for another, imagined that it was the thought of the storm which scared her! Helen bit her lip against a sudden hysteria and almost ran to her room, slamming the door behind her. She must have been mad to feel that way even for a second! Hadn't that first night at the bungalow been warning enough as to how quickly Jacob would take advantage of any sign of weakness?

Her hands shook as she stripped off the sodden clothes and dressed again in white trousers and a long-sleeved lemon cotton shirt, yet when she looked in the mirror to check her appearance she was shocked at her reflection. The fresh clothes had done little to disguise the hectic glitter in her eyes, the flush which ran along each cheekbone. If Jacob saw her still looking like this then he really would start to become suspicious!

Sitting down in front of the mirror, she applied make-up to tone down the wild colour and brushed her hair back from her face and secured it on top of her head in a severe knot, hoping that it would tone down her whole appearance, but it didn't do that. If anything the severe style and lack of colour in her face served to highlight the luminous glitter in her emerald green eyes.

With a groan, Helen wiped the make-up off then ripped the pins out of her hair and ran her fingers through it before dropping her head into her hands in a gesture of despair. All day long she'd thought about what Jacob had told her, and she felt so vulnerable now that all her beliefs had been shaken to their foundations, yet she couldn't afford to let Jacob know she felt that way.

'Are you all right?' Suddenly Jacob was in the room, his voice holding a note of genuine concern as he watched her. Helen straightened, forcing herself to turn and meet his gaze while inside her heart felt as though it was running a race.

'It is customary to knock before you come barging into a room,' she said coldly.

'I did knock. You didn't hear me, obviously.' Unmoved, he came further into the room and lounged indolently against the wall close to where she was sitting

while he subjected her to a thorough scrutiny which made
her want to curl into a ball and hide. He had changed
out of his wet clothes too into jeans and a pale blue
T-shirt, although his feet were bare and his hair lying
slickly against his skull. He looked big and indomitably
male as he stood there staring at her with those eyes
which always seemed to see far too much. Helen picked
up her hairbrush and ran it through the length of her
hair, raising her brows when he continued to watch her
without saying a word.

'I take it that you do have a reason for bursting in
here?'

He smiled as though her annoyance amused him, yet
his voice was perfectly even when he replied. 'I was just
checking that you were all right. You seemed to be taking
a long time.'

'I didn't realise that there was a time limit. Next time
I shall make sure that I give you a detailed account of
what I intend to do and how long it will take me. Will
that suit you?' She set the brush down, staring back at
him until she was forced to drop her eyes, not proof
against the taunting light in his.

'What are you so uptight about, Helen? Surely you're
over-reacting. I did knock, you didn't hear me—end of
story. Or is it?'

She couldn't help but look at him then, driven by
curiosity to know what he meant, and went cold at the
light of speculation in his eyes when they met hers and
held.

'Is there something else bothering you, Helen?' His
voice was velvety, warm and rich as it stroked so deliciously along every one of her raw nerves. Suddenly what
she had felt before in the hall came rushing back to hit

her again, twice as hard. Jacob was an attractive man and she had never been more aware of it than then as she sat there in the bedroom with the storm raging all around them and an even bigger one raging inside her!

'You look scared, Helen, but what of? The storm? Me, perhaps? Or is it the fact that you are starting to have second thoughts about what you feel about me?'

'I—no! Don't be ridiculous!' She jumped up, unable to sit there a moment longer under that searching scrutiny. Crossing the room, she bent to gather up the broken pieces of the lamp, using the few seconds it gave her to try to get herself under control again. It was vital that she play this scene calmly and not give Jacob any evidence to prove his suspicions.

'Why is it ridiculous? I told you something you were unaware of, so logically it must have altered your views somewhat.'

'You told me some sort of a story, Jacob. Why should I believe it?' she stalled.

'It would be silly for me to lie when you can so easily verify it, wouldn't it, Helen?' He laughed softly. 'But what you are saying is that until you have proof that I was telling the truth you don't intend to change your views one iota? You still hate me, in fact?'

He was relentless, pushing her on and on in a direction she didn't want to go. There was danger along this route, she knew, although she couldn't fully have explained how. Tonight of all nights she didn't want this sort of discussion.

'Surely it's a simple enough question, Helen. You have never had any difficulty in expressing your feelings in the past.'

His soft voice seemed to taunt her attempts to hold the situation at bay, filling her with a nervousness she found it hard to disguise. 'I—I can't see any point in repeating myself. You must know how I feel, Jacob.'

She gathered the last sliver of glass into the pile then stood up to fetch the waste-basket. She hadn't realised that Jacob had crossed the room and gasped when she brushed against him. Instinctively she stepped back, her bare foot poised above the pile of glass.

'Careful!' Jacob drew her away from the danger but into a different sort of danger as he continued to hold her long past the point when it was necessary. Helen could feel every inch of his body against her own, could feel the power in the hands which held her, and her heart went wild as it beat inside her. She wanted to drag herself away from him and run, yet somehow she couldn't seem to find the strength as her heart sent the blood singing along her veins.

'Surely you must have thought about what I told you, Helen? Yet you claim it hasn't altered your view of me?' He shook his head, his mouth curved into a smile which made her heart-beat increase a fraction further. 'It's hard to believe you are telling the truth, darling.'

Helen drew in a shuddery breath, willing herself to stay calm. 'Then I suggest you try harder, Jacob. Oh, obviously I have thought about what you said, but until I have spoken to my father and confirmed your story then I shall reserve judgement.'

He laughed aloud, his fingers tightening just a fraction before he moved her safely away from the glass and let her go. 'Spoken like the true sceptic I know you are! Fair enough, Helen, I shall have to leave it at that. It just makes the anticipation all that much sweeter, in fact.'

He turned to fetch the bin and started to drop the glittering slivers of glass into it. Helen studied him uncertainly, itching to ask a question she knew deep down she shouldn't ask. But it was a battle she was destined to lose, of course, as Jacob undoubtedly had known she would.

'Anticipation of what?'

He glanced up from his crouched position, the light from the overhead fitment bouncing off his black hair yet setting his face in shadow. 'Anticipation of the moment when you can no longer hide behind hatred. Perhaps then you will admit how you really feel about me, Helen.'

There was a wealth of meaning in that deep voice. Helen's face went ashen before she suddenly turned on her heel and hurried from the room, but it was impossible to turn her back on what Jacob had meant. If she didn't hate him any longer, then would she suddenly find that she loved him instead?

The idea was crazy, of course; the egotistical ramblings of a man too used to having his own way! Yet it was hard to dismiss it now that the idea had been planted in her mind. Love and hate were two emotions that men and women had been fighting against since the beginning of time, yet to turn from one and embrace the other was too frightening to imagine. Hating Jacob was one thing, loving him would be infinitely worse!

By the time they finished the sketchy meal Helen prepared for them the storm still showed no sign of abating. The electricity had gone off an hour or so before, so Helen had been forced to work by torchlight as she'd prepared sandwiches and cold drinks. Now she stood up and gathered the few dishes on to a tray to carry them over to the sink, ignoring Jacob as he got up and followed her. Conversation had been non-existent throughout the meal. Helen had wanted to find something to say to break the increasing tension but somehow the words wouldn't come and Jacob had made no attempt to help her. What was he thinking now? Was he enjoying the fact that his earlier taunt had had an obvious effect?

The thought annoyed her so much that she slammed the tray down on to the worktop with far more force than necessary, making the china rattle precariously.

'The storm seems to be making you jumpy, Helen, or perhaps something else is bothering you?'

There was no way she was going to touch that with a barge-pole! Helen ran water into the bowl and added an extra large squirt of washing-up liquid, ignoring Jacob completely as she doused the first plate in the sudsy water. He laughed softly, picking up the towel from its rack to dry the plate and set it carefully down on the counter. Helen cast it a venomous glance then turned her attention back to the task, scrubbing the next plate so hard that it was in danger of losing its delicate pattern. Realising what she was doing she went to set it in the rack then jerked her hand back when Jacob reached to take it off her and their hands touched.

The plate teetered on the edge of the draining board until Jacob rescued it, drying it carefully before setting it on top of the other one.

'Do I make you nervous, Helen?' His tone was bland, yet Helen could feel her hand half lifting from the suds as she fought a sudden urge to wipe the undoubtedly mocking smile off his arrogant face.

'Yes!' she snapped back, shooting him a hard glance. 'But then that was your intention, wasn't it, Jacob?'

His eyes flickered briefly with annoyance before he smiled as he tossed the towel aside. 'Then I must apologise. Perhaps it would be better if I left you to it?'

'Perhaps it would.' Helen turned away, washing the cutlery with meticulous thoroughness as she heard Jacob walk towards the door. She sighed softly, letting her hands rest in the water. How much longer would this storm continue? It just seemed to make the whole situation worse.

As though in answer to her silent question, the wind gave another huge roar as it rushed towards the house, beating against the shutters. Instinctively Helen stepped back away from the window then shot a startled glance upwards when there was a thunderous crashing overhead. Suddenly chunks of plaster started raining down on her head and shoulders and she gave a small gasp of alarm.

'Helen!' Jacob's voice was urgent as he rushed into the room. He caught her by the hand and dragged her towards the door so fast that Helen hardly knew what was happening. There was another deafening explosion of sound and as she watched wide-eyed the ceiling and a section of the roof above fell in. Through the gaping hole she could see the broken remains of a palm tree which the wind had uprooted. If Jacob hadn't reacted so swiftly, the whole lot would have come crashing down on top of her.

A shiver ran down her spine at the thought, followed by another until her body seemed to be racked with them as reaction set in. Jacob pulled her almost roughly into his arms and held her tight as he smoothed the hair back from her face, and Helen was shocked to feel him trem-

bling almost as hard as she was. Her eyes lifted to meet
his almost helplessly, and she heard him mutter something harsh before he crushed her mouth under his in a
kiss which held scant finesse but a wealth of feeling
before, just as abruptly, he set her away from him.

'Are you all right? Nothing fell on you?' Even while
he asked the terse questions his hands slid over her
shoulders and down her arms as he searched for any
injuries. Helen took a shuddery breath, trying to quell
the disturbing sensations that kiss had ignited inside her.
She still felt shocked both by what had happened and
Jacob's reaction to it, but she had to get herself under
control and not allow the drama of the situation to push
common sense aside.

She moved away from his seeking hands, running her
fingers over her hair to dislodge the dust and lumps of
plaster clinging to it. 'I'm fine. There's no need to make
a fuss. I haven't suffered any kind of injury.'

Her voice was as cool as she could make it and she
saw Jacob frown narrowly before he replied in tones just
as cool as hers, 'Good. At least we don't have the
problem of your being injured to contend with. You were
lucky, Helen, it was a close call.'

He glanced over her shoulder, his mouth thinning at
what he saw—whether it was the thought of the danger
she'd been in or the damage the tree had caused, Helen
had no idea, but immediately opted for the latter.

'Without a doubt. However, the house doesn't seem
to have fared so well. Do you think any of the other
rooms were damaged?'

'That's what I intend to find out.' Picking up one of
the large battery-run lanterns, Jacob left the kitchen and
Helen followed him from room to room as he made a

thorough inspection, her heart sinking at what they found. The lounge, study and her bedroom had all suffered a similar fate to the kitchen when the tree had fallen, leaving only Jacob's bedroom and the small dining-room intact. Rain was pouring in through the roof in the other rooms, pooling on the wooden floor, soaking into the sofas and rugs.

'Shouldn't we try to move some of the furniture out before it gets damaged?' Helen asked, surveying the ruin of the lounge.

Jacob shook his head. 'No, it's far too risky. The rest of the roof might come in at any moment.'

'Then what are we going to do?' Helen glanced uncertainly at him then stared up through the gaping hole in the ceiling. The storm was even louder now that it had broken into the house, the wind booming around. Jacob was undoubtedly right about the risks but the thought of going out in such a gale wasn't appealing, and she voiced her thoughts aloud. 'I don't fancy being outside in this.'

He smiled grimly, closing the door on the damage. 'Neither do I. Frankly, it would be foolish to go outside in a storm of this magnitude. There is no way that we would make it into town. I had a terrible job getting back here before and the wind wasn't nearly as strong then as it is now.'

'What do you mean? How did you get back before? Did you come by taxi, or what?'

'"By what" sums it up.' He gave a short laugh as he ran his hand through his hair to smooth it back from his forehead. 'I could only find a cab to bring me part of the way. Everyone was too concerned with making preparations for the storm. I had to walk the rest.'

'Walk?' There was no disguising the shock she felt at the revelation. 'But why didn't you stay in town, Jacob? It must have been a nightmare trying to walk back in this!'

'Why? Because you would have been here by yourself, Helen, if I hadn't got back.'

He turned to go into his bedroom, leaving Helen to sort through the mixture of feelings which followed that terse explanation. Jacob had put himself at risk to get back to the bungalow rather than leave her by herself. Perhaps she was being foolish but the realisation made her feel suddenly warm and—and cared for. And that wasn't something she had ever expected to feel around Jacob!

'Here, take this, will you, Helen?'

Jacob suddenly appeared in the hall, his arms full of bedding as he came towards her. Helen automatically took the pillows he held out to her then stared at them in confusion, but he was already making his way across the hall to enter the dining-room. She followed him slowly, stopping uncertainly in the doorway as she watched him drop the pile of quilts and several blankets on to the floor by the table. Kneeling down, he arranged the quilt under the heavy mahogany table then glanced back at her.

'Pass me those pillows, please.'

Helen started towards him then stopped, clutching the pillows to her like some sort of lifeline. Her heart was drumming like crazy although she couldn't understand why. It was just that Jacob seemed to be acting so strangely!

'What are you doing?'

He stood up with a rough, impatient sigh and took the pillows off her, tossing them down on to the quilt before shaking out one of the blankets and arranging it on top. 'Sorting out somewhere safe for us to spend the rest of the night.' He patted the top of the table. 'This is rock-solid, built to last several lifetimes. If any more of the roof comes in then we shall be fairly safe underneath it.'

'Underneath? You mean you intend for us to—to use it as some kind of a shelter?'

'I see you're starting to understand. Good. It's pretty standard practice during violent storms or hurricanes. Here, I'll give you a hand.'

He held his hand out but Helen made no attempt to take it as she stared at the heap of bedding with ever-widening eyes.

'Come on, sweet, what are you afraid of? Surely you can trust yourself to behave with the utmost decorum—seeing that your opinion of me hasn't changed one bit?'

His tone was blatantly taunting, mockery shining in his eyes, and Helen stiffened at once. 'It isn't my behaviour I'm concerned about, Jacob!'

He made a cross over the region of his heart as he grinned at her. 'You have my word, Helen, my love, that I shall be the perfect gentleman. Now come along.'

As though to add weight to his urgings there was a crashing from the lounge as another part of the roof fell in. Helen cast one last lingering look over her shoulder then told herself she was doing the sensible thing. Ignoring Jacob's outstretched hand, she bent down and scooted on to the makeshift bed, moving as far over as she could as Jacob followed her into the cramped space.

He settled himself comfortably on the quilt, stretching his long legs out as he punched a pillow into shape and put it under his head. He glanced at his watch then back at Helen. 'It's nearly ten. I think we should try to get some sleep, because once morning comes we shall have to try to sort this mess out.'

Helen nodded but she made no attempt to lie down even after Jacob had switched off the lantern, plunging the room into darkness. She sat huddled on her side of the strange bed, her knees upbent, her chin resting on them as she listened to the steady measured sound of Jacob's breathing until she knew he was asleep. Only then did she deem it safe to lie down and draw the blanket over her. Something told her it was going to be an exceptionally long night!

CHAPTER NINE

THE storm blew itself out in the early hours of the morning. Helen had lain awake until then, unable to sleep with the sound of the wind roaring all around and the equally disturbing sound of Jacob's quiet breathing. However, she must have drifted off after that because she was woken a short time later by a thunderous crash.

Heart pounding, she shot bolt upright and stared into the darkness, hearing Jacob cursing softly as he started to scramble out from beneath the table. He stopped to pick up the lantern-torch and switch it on, his face set in the eerie glow it cast over the room.

'Stay here, Helen. I'll go and see what's happened now.'

He was gone before she could attempt to stop him, his footsteps echoing as he crossed the hall. Helen counted to ten then re-counted, and when there was no sign of him appearing, scrambled out from under the table and followed him, preferring that to being left wondering and waiting.

It was pitch dark in the hall and she paused, wishing that she had thought to pick up the other smaller torch. She half turned back to find it, then stopped abruptly when from somewhere in the house came another loud crash followed by a sharp exclamation. Forgetting all about the need for light, she stumbled towards the sound, her voice reflecting her fear as she called Jacob's name.

'In here—the study, but don't try and come in, Helen.'

135

She could have wept when Jacob answered her immediately, allaying the worst of her fears. She ran to the open study door and peered into the room then visibly jumped when he suddenly appeared out of the darkness. In the glow from the torch she could see plaster dust clinging to his clothes and coating his skin and hair. When he took her arm and hurried her back to the dining-room, she went without a protest, waiting until they were both safely in the shelter of the table before asking any questions.

'What happened? Did the ceiling come down on you?'

He nodded briefly as he eased himself into a more comfortable position and wiped the gritty grey dust off his face with the back of his hand. 'Yes. It was my own stupid fault, of course. I should never have gone into the room but I suddenly remembered that I had left some papers on the desk and went in to move them. The next thing I knew there were lumps of plaster and tiles dropping all over me.' He ran his hand lightly across his left shoulder and grimaced. 'I caught quite a bit of it on my shoulder.'

'Are you hurt? Let me see.' Helen picked up the torch and directed its beam on to Jacob, gasping in dismay when she saw the blood on his T-shirt. 'It's bleeding, Jacob. Take your shirt off and let me see how bad it is.'

He shook his head. 'It's fine. There's no need to fuss.'

'Don't be silly. It isn't fussing to see how bad it is. Now please take that T-shirt off!'

'Yes, ma'am.' He smiled with gentle mockery at the authoritative note in her voice but started to drag the dusty shirt over his head, unable to disguise his gasp of pain as he raised his arms to pull it off.

'Here, let me help.' As gently as possible Helen eased the shirt over his head, biting her lip when she saw his mouth thin as she was forced to raise his left arm to get it free. Tossing it on to the quilt, she picked by the torch and focused the beam on Jacob's shoulder to examine the long gash which was still oozing blood. The flesh surrounding the cut was turning purple, evidence if she'd needed it of the bruise he was going to have in a very short time.

'It probably looks far worse than it is.'

Jacob's voice was deliberately reassuring and for some reason Helen could have hit him. There was no need to play the big tough hero; she wasn't about to fall into a heap at his feet, fainting from the sight of the injury! It must hurt like crazy and he was being stupid to try to pretend otherwise just to spare her.

She glared at him, her small face set, her eyes glittering with annoyance. 'I doubt that! Honestly, Jacob, I just don't believe that you were going to try to pass that off as nothing! It needs cleaning, dressing and covering to stop any dirt getting into it and starting up an infection.'

She started to scramble out from under the table, then stopped abruptly when he caught her arm. 'And where do you think you're going?'

She eased her arm out of his hold and smiled thinly at him. 'To find something to put on that shoulder of yours, of course.'

'There is no of course about it! I'm not letting you go anywhere, Helen. I can manage perfectly well until the morning.'

'Perhaps you can, but I don't intend to let you. That cut needs attending to, Jacob, and I mean to make sure that it is treated.'

Without giving him a chance to argue further, Helen scrambled out from under the table and hurried from the room, ignoring Jacob's angry roar to come back. As quickly as she could she made her way by torchlight to the bedroom Jacob had been using, which seemed to be relatively unscathed so far. Hurrying into the *en suite* bathroom, she ran water into the basin and soaked a towel in it then wrung it out and on a sudden impulse opened the cabinet and sorted through the contents, smiling when she found not only some gauze dressings but a tube of antiseptic cream as well.

'Has anyone told you that you would try the patience of a saint sometimes?' Jacob stood in the doorway watching her, the light from the small torch he was carrying casting a dim glow over his face so that it seemed all hard angles. Helen shot him a wary glance then turned back to her task, adding a few more items to the small pile she had amassed, forcing herself to concentrate on the task at hand and keep her thoughts away from the sight he made standing there, his black hair ruffled, his powerful chest bare. Suddenly the very air between them seemed to throb with a danger which owed little to the situation they were in. It was as though the storm had ripped through the house and carried away with it all the safety barriers she had sheltered behind. Now there was just her and Jacob and this strange new awareness she felt which scared her.

'You are far from being a saint, Jacob,' she replied softly as she gathered up the pile of first-aid items and wrapped them in another towel to carry them back to the dining-room.

He laughed shortly. 'Meaning that I am more of a sinner? Is that how you see me, Helen?'

She stopped what she was doing, her eyes lifting to meet his across the room while her heart seemed to go wild. 'I used to think that was what you were.'

'And now?' Jacob's voice sounded suddenly harsh and strained and Helen stiffened, wondering if it was wise to continue this oddly unsettling conversation. Why did she have the sudden feeling that her reply was important to him? She searched his dark face but it was impossible to guess, impossible to read anything of what he was thinking with only the dim light from the torch to see by.

She turned away as she picked up the bundle and gave a small shrug. 'And now I think the most important thing is to get that cut seen to.'

She started towards the door, then slowed uncertainly when Jacob made no attempt to get out of her way. He stood and watched her, his gaze never wavering from her face until Helen could feel the colour stealing under her skin, feel her heart beating faster. He seemed to be searching for his own answers to his own questions, answers she wasn't sure she wanted him to find. Once, not so long ago, everything had been so clear; she had known exactly what she thought of Jacob. Now the image she had held of him was slowly distorting, losing its clearly defined limits, and she was afraid of what she might find beneath the tough exterior he presented to the world.

'One day you will have to give me a proper answer, Helen. You won't be able to evade doing that forever.'

'I have no idea what you're talking about. Now don't you think it would be sensible to go back to the dining-room? There's no knowing if more of the roof is going to start falling in at any moment.'

She edged past him, her footsteps quickening as she crossed the hall, although it wasn't fear of the roof falling which caused her to hurry. She wanted to put an end to that disturbing conversation and all the uncertainties it aroused in her. Perhaps she would have to face up to how she felt about Jacob some time soon, but not now, not while that tension existed between them. She couldn't afford to be influenced into making a mistake.

Kneeling down beside the table, she laid the towel on top of the quilt and spread the collection of cream and dressings neatly along it, then glanced back over her shoulder at Jacob who was standing just behind her. 'If you sit down here on the edge of the quilt then I can wash that cut and put a dressing on it.'

She kept her tone coolly impersonal and saw him give a faintly mocking smile. Obviously he understood her desire to defuse the situation. However, he made no comment as he sat down as directed, positioning himself next to her on the quilt. Helen took a few seconds to angle the torch so that light fell on to his bruised shoulder, then set to work with the wet towel cleaning away the dried blood from around the cut. Now that the wind had died down, everywhere seemed un-naturally silent. There was just the soft brush of the cloth against Jacob's skin, the sound of their quiet breathing. It seemed to heighten the feeling of intimacy and her hands shook as she smoothed the wet cloth once again over the angry-looking gash.

'How bad is it?'

She jerked her hands away from him when he suddenly spoke, then forced herself to carry on, spreading antiseptic cream on to a piece of sterile gauze dressing she removed from its package. 'It doesn't look too deep. I'm no expert but I don't think it will need stitching, although you're going to find your shoulder will be stiff and sore tomorrow, I expect.'

'I'm sure I shall survive.'

'I'm sure you will too. A little thing like this won't be enough to set you back, Jacob. You're far too tough for that!'

There was a sharp bite to her tone and his eyes narrowed. Reaching up, he caught her hand and held it. 'I've always had to be tough, Helen, and I won't apologise for it now.'

'No one asked you to! I was merely stating a fact!' She couldn't explain why she suddenly felt so angry. There was no logical explanation why, yet she could feel the anger building inside her.

'Stating a fact or making an accusation?' Jacob's temper was rising to meet hers, his eyes glittering with it as they met hers and held. 'My so-called toughness is just another strike against me in your eyes, isn't it, Helen?'

'Yes!' She spat the answer back at him. 'You aren't like other men, Jacob! You won't admit when you're hurt or in pain. You consider it a sign of weakness!'

'And can you blame me?' His fingers tightened around hers, holding her fast when she would have pulled away. 'I learned early on that if you show weakness then someone will use it against you! Do you imagine that I could have built the business I now own up to what it is if I had done?' He shook his head, his face set into harsh lines of anger. 'I had to be tough and uncompromising and ruthless to get what I wanted. I fought day and night, week in and week out, until I had a toe-hold on the ladder, then had to fight even harder to hold on to what I had.' He laughed shortly, tossing her hand away from him. 'I still have to fight even now because there is always someone, somewhere who will try to take what you have achieved away from you, so don't accuse me of being tough and mean it as an insult! In my book it's a virtue!'

'Even when it leaves no room for tenderness or compassion? You're a coward, Jacob Hunt, because you are simply afraid to show those feelings!' All of a sudden tears were stinging her eyes and she blinked them away, unable to explain what had caused them. It had just been what Jacob had said, the way he had said it. He sounded like a man who cared for no one and nothing apart from what he wanted from life, and it made her ache.

'Oh, you're wrong, Helen. I am capable of feeling and showing both tenderness and compassion and a whole lot more—to the right person.'

There was something in his voice which made her heart beat faster, made her breath catch. Helen stared at him in confusion and felt colour touch her cheeks when she saw the light in his eyes. Suddenly, in the space of a single heartbeat the tension in the room shifted away from anger to another emotion equally strong which made her feel afraid.

'Jacob, I don't...'

He laughed deeply, leaning slowly towards her to catch her chin and tilt her face so that she was forced to meet his glittering gaze. 'Now who is the coward, my love? You accuse me of being one, but you are just as guilty.'

'No. Please stop! This is not going to achieve anything.' She caught at his restraining fingers, but although he dropped his hand from her chin he continued to hold her, his hand warm and hard against the flesh of her upper arm through the thin cotton shirt.

'I disagree. I think this could achieve a great deal for both of us, Helen.' He studied her wide eyes, then let his gaze drop to her mouth, his own lips curving as it parted slightly under the hot gaze from his eyes. Helen swallowed hard, trying to ease the huge knot of tension which threatened to choke her as she strove for calm.

'Be sensible, Jacob,' she said hoarsely. 'This isn't the answer to anything. It will just create more problems!'

'You're wrong, sweet. This is something you and I should have sorted out years ago. Maybe then both our lives would have turned out differently.'

'I don't know what you're talking about! We have nothing to sort out—nothing apart from what you have done to my family!' She pulled against his hold but he drew her closer, so close that she could feel the heat from his bare skin against her breasts, and every nerve in her body jolted in a wild reaction to the sensation.

'I have already explained that my part in it wasn't what you imagined.'

'Yes, you have, but until I have positive proof that you were telling the truth then it means nothing to me, Jacob. Nothing! Understand?'

'I understand. I understand that you are scared of facing up to the truth, scared of having to admit at long last that I am guilty of nothing apart from trying to help you.' His voice dropped as his hands slid down her arms, smoothing the cotton against her skin, caressing her through the thin material. 'And scared of having finally to face up to your real feelings for me.'

'No! I am not scared of anything, Jacob Hunt—least of all how I feel about you!' The words were no sooner out of her mouth than Helen wished she could take them back. They had sounded like a direct challenge even to her, and as she cast a wary glance at Jacob she knew that was how he considered them. When he bent towards her she gave a sharp little cry of alarm, her hands lifting unthinkingly to push him away. He groaned deeply as her fingers bit into the wound on his shoulder, his eyes closing briefly at the sharp stabbing pain.

Helen froze, her hands resting on his shoulders as she watched him. 'I'm sorry,' she said dully. 'I didn't mean to hurt you like that.'

His eyes opened slowly. 'We've been hurting each other since we first met, Helen. Don't you think it's time that we stopped and gave each other pleasure instead?'

His head dipped towards her, intent written clearly on his face and in the hot depths of his eyes, and Helen turned her head away. 'No! Don't, Jacob. I don't want you to kiss me!'

He laughed harshly, scornfully, a rim of colour edging his angular cheekbones. 'Don't you? Are you sure? It seems to me that your head says one thing while your body says something entirely different.' He slid his hand down her throat and let his fingers lie against the pulse which was beating crazily at the base of her neck.

'Of course I'm sure! I know how I feel and I don't want you to kiss me! So please let me go.' She didn't want to hurt him again, but if he didn't stop this then she might be forced to do so. Yet even as the thought ran through her head, Jacob forestalled any attempts she might have made to push him away. Capturing her hands, he eased them behind her back to bring her into abrupt contact with his naked chest as he smiled into her shocked face.

'What you want is convincing that I am right.' He ran his hand up her body from hip to breast, his fingers smoothing deliberately across the soft curves before he stared meaningfully down at where her nipples were thrusting against the thin cotton blouse in blatant response to his touch.

Colour flooded her face and she looked away. 'I hate you, Jacob,' she said hoarsely.

'Maybe, but that isn't what you are feeling most right now, is it, my sweet little coward? It isn't hatred which heats your blood and makes your body respond so eagerly.' His head came down and he took her mouth in a harsh kiss which made no concessions. His lips were unrelenting, demanding a response. Helen twisted and turned but it was impossible to free herself from the iron-hard grip of his hands, just as it was impossible to evade the seeking mouth which covered hers. There was no softness in the rawly savage kiss, no tenderness, and something inside her cried out against the cold deliberation of it.

Tears slid from her eyes, running down her cheeks to slide into the corner of her mouth, and Jacob must have tasted their saltiness because he drew back abruptly, his face set as he studied her. Helen could hear the rasping sound of his breathing mingling with her own, and the sounds filled her with pain. Jacob could only feel contempt for her to kiss her that way and, although she claimed to hate him, it hurt to realise it.

The thought made the tears flow faster, and she heard him utter a rough exclamation before he drew her to him and held her with a gentleness she had never expected after that rough assault. 'Don't cry. I can't bear to see you crying and know that it's my fault!'

His lips skimmed her temple, pushing the heavy fall of hair aside to brush her skin in a caress which sent a tremor shooting through her. Jacob must have felt it because he let her go at once, his face bleak. 'I would never hurt you physically, Helen. Surely you must know that I could never do that!'

There was such stark pain in his voice that she replied instinctively to soothe it. 'I know that, Jacob.'

'Then why are you trembling?' He got up abruptly and walked across the darkened room, then came back and slammed his fist against the top of the table in a gesture which shocked her. Jacob never lost control and to see him doing so now made everything seem suddenly unimportant, everything apart from telling him the truth. She owed him that much at least.

'I—I'm not afraid of you, Jacob. It wasn't fear which made me tremble like that.' Her voice was so low that it barely disturbed the silence, and she thought he hadn't heard her at first as he stood there, his shoulders hunched, his whole body rigid. Then suddenly he knelt down on the edge of the quilt, his face just inches away from hers as he stared straight into her eyes with an expression in his which made her breath catch, made the blood swell in her veins.

'Then what was it, Helen? Tell me!'

His voice seemed to vibrate through her whole body until she felt dizzy with the sensations it aroused. Through a haze she watched him move closer, so close that if she reached out her hand she could have smoothed the frown from between his eyes, could have laid her hand against his hard, warm chest and felt his heart tapping out a rhythm as fast and as furious as the one beating inside her. And it was that realisation which pushed her into doing something which, deep down, she knew she would come to regret.

'Not fear, Jacob, but desire.'

There was a moment, just one, when the words seemed to hang suspended, when she had the feeling that Jacob didn't dare believe them, then it was gone as he came down beside her on the quilt and took her into his arms. This time his mouth was warm and mobile as it took hers, his lips inviting rather than demanding a response, and Helen found herself unable to refuse. She had accused Jacob of being emotionless but there was such emotion in the way his mouth moved over hers while his hands stroked her body that she felt almost overwhelmed by the intensity of it.

'Helen—sweet Helen. You don't know how long I've waited for this!' There was a raw ache of need in his voice which tugged at her emotions and she arched towards him, wanting to give him all he sought. He murmured something softly under his breath then slowly laid her down on the quilt, his eyes filled with a desire he made no attempt to hide as he bent over her and kissed her cheeks, her chin, the smooth curve of her jaw before letting his mouth stop on the delicate curl of her ear while he nibbled kisses around its rim.

Helen felt a wave of desire surge inside her and she clung to him, letting her fingers smooth over the strong muscles in his back and shoulders, feeling them clench under her touch. Deliberately she smoothed her hands across them again, loving the smoothness of Jacob's skin, the burning heat beneath, the long shudder he gave which told her more clearly than anything just how he felt. Jacob had always been so strong and in control before, and now this sudden vulnerability he betrayed excited her almost beyond bearing.

She shifted on the tumble of quilts and blankets and heard him groan roughly as his hand ran down her body to still her movements. 'God, Helen, don't do that! You've got me so het up I can barely think!'

She smiled against his cheek, letting her lips feather small kisses along the faintly rough skin of his jaw before lifting her head to press more against the smooth curve of his brows. 'My, what a confession, Jacob! I never thought I would live to see the day when you admitted you weren't fully in control!'

He laughed aloud at her blatantly provocative teasing, his hand covering her breast as he teased the already rigid nipple through the thin barrier of shirt and bra. Helen gasped at the sensations which spun like silk through each limb, soft yet dangerously seductive. 'And I never thought the day would finally come when I might make that admission!'

He kissed her again, his lips so achingly tender that she never wanted the kiss to stop, and clung to him when he tried to move away. He smiled down into her eyes, then smoothed another fleetingly sweet kiss against her mouth before dropping his gaze to her blouse as slowly, one by one, he worked the buttons free. Helen lay quite still, scarcely breathing as the final one opened and Jacob lifted the two sides of the shirt apart then unfastened the tiny clip at the front of her bra and smoothed it away from her breasts. He stared down at her for a long

moment then lifted his eyes to hers, and something inside
Helen seemed to swell until it filled her with warmth as
she saw the expression almost of reverence in his glittering gaze.

'You're beautiful, Helen, so very beautiful. Just as I
always knew you would be.'

'Jacob!' His name was soft the way she said it in that
whispery little voice, yet it seemed to hold a wealth of
meaning. It made no attempt to hide the desire she could
feel inside her but issued an invitation which Jacob
wasn't slow to hear. His face went still, his eyes blazing
in the dim light from the torch, every hard muscle in his
chest and shoulders clearly defined as though he were
holding himself in check. Then with a low groan of part
defeat and part triumph he slid down beside her on the
quilt and took her into his arms, his hungry mouth and
clever hands teaching her about feelings and sensations
she had never known existed until then.

And later when Jacob drove them both towards diz-
zying, magical heights to find a completion which left
her shuddering helplessly in his strong arms, Helen knew
that, whatever she felt about this man who was her
husband, it wasn't hatred.

CHAPTER TEN

DAWN broke in a blaze of colour, as though nature was trying to atone for the havoc it had wrought the night before.

Helen stood on the veranda watching the sky turn from crimson to gold. The beach was littered with debris carried ashore by the storm and fronds of the palm trees which the wind had ripped off. Jacob's yacht had been beached and was lying on its side, the mast split in two, a huge gaping hole in the once spotless white hull. The storm had caused a vast amount of damage to the property and undoubtedly to the rest of the island, but eventually it would all be cleared up. If only it were so easy to clear up all the other reminders the storm had left behind. If the night hadn't been so fraught and tense, then would she have made love so willingly with Jacob? Surely that had been the reason why she had acted the way she had!

'It's a real mess, isn't it?'

She hadn't realised that he had woken up and stiffened at the sound of his voice, her face colouring hectically. But when she finally summoned up the courage to glance at Jacob as he came to join her, she realised that he had been referring to the storm damage to the property.

She nodded briefly, turning her eyes away from him, hating the way her heart gave a shuddering lurch as the memories came flooding back, so clear and so strong that she didn't think she could cope with them now in the revealing light of day. She didn't hate Jacob, that much she knew, yet something inside her shied away from admitting exactly how she did feel about him. She needed more time to come to terms with what had happened between them, but as she murmured an excuse and turned to hurry back inside she knew that Jacob had no intention of affording her any time.

He stepped in front of her, big and powerful as he stood there and watched her in silence until the colour filled her cheeks. Helen dropped her eyes away from the glittering intensity of his gaze, twisting her fingers nervously against the dusty white fabric of her jeans while she tried to find something to say, words to make Jacob understand how she felt, but whatever she thought of sounded too revealing.

'You can't pretend it never happened, Helen. I won't let you do that.'

His voice was harsh, uncompromising, and her heart started to thump sickeningly hard inside her chest as she heard it. Perhaps if he had shown a touch of compassion then maybe she could have told him how confused she felt, but there was no way she could make such a confession now.

Her head came up and she met his cold gaze, fighting against a sudden wave of pain. 'I am quite sure that you won't, Jacob. I'm not fool enough to imagine that.'

His mouth thinned but he replied levelly enough. 'Then you must understand that it isn't possible to ignore what we did. We made love last night, Helen, not because I forced you but because you wanted to as much as I did. There is no way that you can run away from that fact!'

'Perhaps not, but neither does it mean that I want to repeat it!' His unyielding attitude hurt and she responded to it in the only way she could without breaking down. '*Yes*, we did make love, Jacob, and *no*, you didn't need to force me. As you said, I was perfectly willing.' She shrugged lightly, glancing past him as she fought for the control to carry on when it felt as though her heart was being slowly ripped to shreds inside her. Didn't Jacob know how difficult this was for her? Didn't he care? Apparently not.

'Yet you have no intention of allowing it to happen again at some future date?' He laughed softly, dangerously as he took a step closer to her. 'Come on, Helen! Who are you kidding? It won't be a question of your allowing me to make love to you, doling out favours when and if you feel that way inclined! You wanted me as much as I wanted you, and that desire will be the deciding factor in the future as it was last night.'

His hand shot out, pulling her into his arms so abruptly that she slammed against his chest and lay there for a stunned moment before starting to struggle wildly. 'No! There won't be any future occasions, Jacob. Last night was a one-off, and was it any wonder with the storm and everything? Feelings were heightened by the danger we were in and——'

'You honestly believe that? That the storm was the reason for it?' He laughed aloud, his face set into lines of mockery as he tilted her face and stared down into her emerald eyes, then allowed his gaze to drop deliberately to her mouth then further to the curve of her breasts under the cotton blouse, and Helen was filled with shame when she felt her body respond immediately to the look.

She wrenched herself away from his hold, panic rippling along her veins before she brought it under control. 'That proves nothing, Jacob. Nothing! All right, so I do respond to your touch, but any woman would.' Her eyes shone with scorn. 'You're a skilled lover, Jacob. You know exactly what to do to get the response you want, and I am no different from any other woman. But that's all it was, an instinctive physical response. So please don't flatter yourself into imagining that it meant more than that, because it didn't!'

'I see.' He leant back against the veranda rail, folding his arms across his chest as he watched her through hooded eyes. His chest was still bare, and against his tanned skin the white gauze on his shoulder made a startling contrast. Even though he'd had little sleep and hadn't shaved he still looked stunningly attractive, and Helen felt the blood start to run hotly through her veins as she watched him and remembered the intimacies they had shared just hours before.

'I suppose I could accept that, Helen, if it weren't for one small fact.'

'And that is?' It was hard to hide the nervousness she felt, hard to control the rush of disturbing memories of those hours she had lain in his arms.

'That until last night you were a virgin.' His soft voice brought her back to the present abruptly. Helen stared at him with a mounting fear, watching the way his mouth curled slowly into a smile which held a wealth of meaning. 'Did you think I wouldn't realise that, my sweet? Granted, your response was delightfully enthusiastic, but it owed little to experience, did it? So tell me why, if wanting to make love is purely a matter of pushing the right buttons, so to speak, you haven't tried it before—with Richard, perhaps? You and he seemed to be close, so surely it would have been a natural progression in your relationship? Yet until last night when the storm struck and I just happened to be around, you were never tempted? Seems odd to me, Helen but perhaps there is something I'm missing?'

'I—I...' She stopped abruptly, unable to think of what to say in reply to the taunting statements. Jacob was right; until last night she had never made love to any man, never wanted to, yet she had wanted him with a desire which defied all attempts at logic.

'You have always professed to hate me, Helen, even last night, but can you honestly say with your hand on your heart that's how you still feel now?' His voice was rock-steady as it asked a question which shook her with fear. Her eyes skittered to his face then away as she drew a quick desperate breath, but it did little to stem the feeling that she was teetering on the edge of some great precipice. She felt so confused, her head whirling with questions, feelings, emotions, all mixed up with this sharp fear that one small step could send her plunging over the edge into a situation far worse than any she had encountered so far.

'Helen? Aren't you going to answer me?' He was relentless as he pushed her on and on towards an answer which was whispering at the very edge of her consciousness, trying to make itself heard, but her fear was just too strong; fear that she might not be able to cope with the repercussions once she allowed it into the open.

'Last night changes nothing, Jacob.'

He pushed away from the rail to tower over her for a moment before starting back inside the house. He paused to look back, the sunlight catching him to turn his skin

to bronze, his eyes jewel-bright as they rested on Helen's
face in a look she could feel, before he gave a small,
confident smile. 'All right, Helen, I'll let it go at that
for now. But very soon now you will have to face up to
the truth.' He laughed softly, the breeze carrying the
sound and magnifying it. 'Last night we moved a lot
closer to achieving that!'

He disappeared inside the house, and Helen turned
away to grip the rail with numb fingers as she stared out
to sea and felt the fear inside her swamp her. She didn't
want to face the truth of how she felt about Jacob! He
was a man used to power, used to using it to get what
he wanted, and instinct told her that it would be handing
him a huge amount of power over her, leaving her completely vulnerable to whatever he chose to do. Yet if she
stayed with him then he would push her day after day
into admitting how she felt, slowly gain that much more
power over her life. She couldn't bear that to happen.
Their marriage had been a mistake from the start and
now what she must do was rectify it as quickly as possible
and save herself from making any more, far more dis-
astrous mistakes!

It was almost evening when Helen arrived back in
London. She took a taxi from the airport to the flat and
let herself in, relieved to find that it was empty. Obviously
her father was still at the house, and, although she would
have to go to see him and explain what she had decided,
she wouldn't need to do so immediately.

Carrying her bag through to the sitting-room, she sank
down on to the sofa and closed her eyes as weariness
overcame her. Jacob had been out when she had left,
trying to arrange some help to clear up the damage

caused by the storm. Helen had waited until he had gone then rushed around packing a few things into a bag, all the time afraid that he would come back and discover what she was up to. However, by the time the taxi had arrived to take her to the airport there was still no sign of him.

He must have found the note she'd left for him by now, so what would he do? She wasn't fool enough to imagine that would be the end of it. No, Jacob would come after her, but suddenly Helen felt too tired to worry about it. At least she'd gained some breathing space to muster her arguments and try to make him understand what a mistake their marriage had been.

Sighing, she got up to take her bag through to her room, then stopped when the doorbell suddenly rang. For a moment panic overwhelmed her before she came to her senses and realised that it couldn't possibly be Jacob so soon. She had managed to get the last available seat on the flight back to London and there wouldn't be another free for several days.

Anxious to get rid of the unwanted caller she hurried to the door, then felt her stomach give a sickening lurch when she discovered Richard outside.

'Helen, how are you? I must confess that I was surprised to see you back from your honeymoon so soon *and* minus your husband. What went wrong, darling? Did you suddenly realise what a fool you had been to get mixed up with a bastard like Hunt?'

Helen forced herself to meet Richard's taunting gaze, refusing to reply to the question. 'What do you want, Richard? And how did you discover that I was home?'

He laughed in a way which sent a shiver crawling down her spine. 'I saw you at the airport. I was just on my way to book in for a flight back to the States when I spotted you and I thought I couldn't possibly miss the opportunity to catch up on what has been happening to you, especially as your husband wasn't with you.' He took a step towards the door, his smile thinning when Helen made no attempt to let him in.

'I see. However, I am sure you will understand that I am rather busy right now, so if you will——'

'Oh, no, Helen. You aren't getting rid of me that easily. Not until we've had a chance to talk and I've told you my news.' He forced the door open so that he could step inside the hall, then glanced mockingly back at her. 'If you're worried about a repeat of the last time I paid you a visit, then don't be. I don't have any inclination to take another man's leftovers. You chose Hunt and you're welcome to him. It's just a shame that you are probably going to regret it.'

There was something in Richard's voice which made the hairs on the back of Helen's neck rise. Slowly she closed the door, her eyes never leaving his face, but he merely afforded her a taunting smile as he walked through to the sitting-room and sat down. There was a glitter of excitement in his eyes as he watched her follow him, a pent-up tension which alarmed her even though she had no idea what was causing it. She had known Richard for some time, yet suddenly she had the strangest feeling that she was seeing a stranger.

'Aren't you curious about what I meant just now, Helen?' He relaxed back in the chair and crossed his legs, making no attempt to hide his amusement. Helen took a slow breath then forced herself to take the chair opposite him.

'I'm sure you intend to tell me whether I'm curious or not, so let's hear it, Richard. What is this earth-shattering piece of news you are longing to tell me?'

He sat up abruptly, his mouth drawing into lines of anger as he recognised the sarcasm in her voice. Helen wondered how she had never noticed before just how different he looked when he was annoyed. They had argued infrequently, mainly because she had never cared enough to make an issue about most of the things they had disagreed on, yet somehow it had never struck her so forcibly just how Richard's expression could change when he was crossed.

'I am sure you'll be laughing on the other side of your face soon, Helen. You and that husband of yours!' He laughed harshly, the sound grating in the silence. 'Did you really think that I would let you both get away with making a fool of me?'

'Neither Jacob nor I ever intended that! And I resent your accusing me of it, Richard.'

'Don't bother getting on your high horse with me, sweet. I know what happened! You led me on until something better came along, or rather someone with more money, that is. That was the deciding factor, wasn't it? Jacob Hunt could buy and sell me a thousand times over and still have change in his pocket. And that was the real reason why you decided to marry him!'

'No!' Helen jumped to her feet, her face flaming at the accusation. 'How dare you say that? You're wrong.'

'Am I?' He shrugged carelessly. 'I don't think so. In fact, I know I'm not. I've been hearing a few stories about you lately, Helen; about the fact that Hunt has been paying all your bills at this flat, not to mention the fact that he owns it and simply allowed you and your father to live here. That is something you just forgot to mention to me, of course. Still, it makes no difference now. As far as I'm concerned Hunt bought what you were willing to sell, so it seems that you both got what you wanted—and deserve. I wonder, though, if you'll think it was worth it in a few days' time? Perhaps then you will start to see what a mistake you made.'

He stood up and smiled at her, and Helen unconsciously shrank away from the hatred she could see burning in his eyes. 'You married Hunt for his money, so how will you feel when you suddenly discover that he hasn't got a penny, that the whole lot has gone? Will that make you reconsider this marriage of yours, Helen?'

'What are you talking about? Has—has something happened to Jacob's business?' It was hard to control the fear she felt, but she struggled to do so as she tried to make Richard explain.

'Mmm, you might say that. You see, Helen, I wasn't at all happy with the way things turned out, and put my mind to doing something constructive about it. And would you believe that fate was on my side?' He glanced at his watch then back at her. 'I wish I could stay to explain more fully but I do have that plane to catch.' He walked to the door, then stopped to look back. 'I hope Hunt thinks that you were worth it, because very soon you are going to be all he has left, and that is assuming that you decide to stay with him, which I doubt. Goodbye, Helen. I don't imagine that our paths will cross again so I wish you luck. You and your husband are going to need it. Oh, and if Hunt ever asks why it happened then don't be shy, tell him straight that it was all because of you!'

He left, closing the door quietly behind him. Helen stared at it with wide, shocked eyes as she tried to make sense of what he had said, but that was impossible without knowing more details. She ran after Richard but when she reached the foyer there was no sign of him there nor in the driveway outside. He must have had a taxi waiting for him and left at once.

Slowly she made her way back to the flat and closed the door again, her whole body cold with fear. If only she knew what Richard had done then maybe she could have found some way to rectify the damage, but she had no idea what form his revenge had taken. How bitterly ironic that after everything that had happened and her final realisation that Jacob wasn't to blame, he might suffer because of her! Yet somehow she had to find a means to stop it happening if she could, even if it meant contacting Jacob.

Three hours later, Helen put the telephone down for the last time, admitting that she was beaten. She had tried more than a dozen times to get through to Nassau and each time met with the same courteous response, informing her that the storm had made communications impossible at present but to try again in the morning when, hopefully, the faults would have been cleared. All she could do now was follow that advice, but it wasn't easy knowing that Jacob was in danger of losing everything unless she found some means to prevent it.

Still worrying about it, Helen switched off the sitting-room lamps then went to her room and undressed. Pulling on a thick fluffy towelling robe she made her way to the bathroom and ran the shower. The water was deliciously warm, soothing some of the tension from her body, and she stayed in it for ages until finally she switched it off. She reached for a towel to dry herself then stopped when she caught sight of her reflection in the mirror over the basin.

There was a small dark bruise on the top of her arm and she touched a fingertip to it, remembering with an achingly vivid clarity how it had happened last night when Jacob had been unconsciously rough in his lovemaking. His hands had gripped her arms, his blue eyes burning with desire as he had stared down at her in the very moment when his body had joined with hers in the final act of possession.

'Jacob!' His name was no more then a whisper as it fell from her lips but it filled her mind and body with his presence. They had spent such a short time together in their bitter marriage, yet suddenly Helen knew that no matter what happened she didn't regret it. Jacob had said that it would be a chance for them to discover new things about each other, and he had been right. Jacob wasn't the man she had thought him to be. He was tough and uncompromising, but he had a strength a weaker person could lean on. He was ruthless in his drive to get to the top, but he would never ask more of another person than he was prepared to give himself tenfold. He hadn't set out to ruin her father, but had offered help when it was desperately needed. She had been so very, very wrong about him for all these years and now he was going to suffer because of it.

She turned away from the mirror and ran a hand across her eyes to wipe away the fruitless tears, then slipped the robe back on to make her way back to her bedroom. She paused uncertainly in the hallway as she saw the light spilling from the sitting-room. She could have sworn she'd switched all the lamps off before, but then she'd had her mind on other things.

Walking swiftly into the room, Helen went to the desk and bent to switch the lamp off, then stilled with shock when a familiar voice spoke. 'Leave it on, Helen. You and I have a lot to discuss before this night is over.'

For a second she couldn't seem to move let alone speak, her hand poised above the switch, her body rigid with shock. Then Jacob continued and broke the spell he had cast on her.

'Damn you, Helen, don't you think I deserve more? At least the courtesy of your waiting to say goodbye rather than taking off the way you did?'

There was no mistaking Jacob's anger, and Helen steeled herself as she stood up and turned to look at him. For a moment her gaze lingered on the hard set of his jaw, the glint of steel in his deep blue eyes before she looked away and took a shuddering, desperate little breath which did nothing to steady the crazy tempo of her heartbeat.

'How did you manage to get here so fast? There were no seats left, I was told. I—I've been trying to contact you all evening.'

'Have you? Why? Struck by a sudden attack of conscience, were you, my sweet?' He smiled as he walked across the room towards her. 'I find that hard to believe. But for your information I chartered a plane to fly me back. Fortunately I had kept hold of a key to the flat so had no difficulty in letting myself in.' He laughed softly, scant amusement in the sound of his voice. 'Did you really think that I would let you go like that, Helen?'

'I left you a note, Jacob. It—it explained why I had decided to go.' She wished her voice didn't sound so reedy-thin, but it was the way he was looking at her, his face filled with icy contempt. Abruptly she turned away to pour herself a drink she didn't want, and sipped it while she watched him over the rim of the glass.

'Ah, yes—the note. We mustn't forget that. Was that why you were trying to contact me, darling? To make sure that I had found it? I did, of course.' He dug his hand into the pocket of his jeans and pulled out a crumpled piece of paper, tossing it on to the table next to her. 'It was all very clear, Helen. Did it take you long to work out what you would write to get it down in such precise terms?'

'Our marriage was a mistake, Jacob. You must realise that as I do. It will be better for both of us if we accept that and end it.'

'So you think that divorce is the answer?'

Helen's heart gave a shuddering lurch at the thought, but she nodded. 'Surely it makes sense?'

'Perhaps it does—to you.' He took another slow step towards her, his voice grating with anger. 'Did you have this all planned right from the beginning, darling?'

'I don't know what you mean!' She backed away from him until she came up against the edge of the table, afraid of the fury she could sense building in him.

'Why be coy? It must give you a certain satisfaction to see your plans reach fruition the way they seem to have done.'

'You're talking in riddles, Jacob! Unless you care to explain then I can't see any——'

'Oh, I'll be happy to explain just so that we have it all out in the open, so that you know that I understand what you were up to.' With lightning speed his hand snaked out to catch her wrist and pull her to him so that he could glare down into her white face. 'It was well done, I'll give you that. Last night you let me make love to you, although perhaps you hadn't allowed for the fact that you might enjoy it as you did, and that's why you were so upset this morning. Then you waited your opportunity and walked out, leaving behind that careful little note informing me that you think it better if we end our marriage and that I should start divorce proceedings.' He hooked a finger under her chin to lift her face so that he could look straight into her eyes. 'That was the real *coup de grâce*, wasn't it, sweet?'

'You're wrong, Jacob! It wasn't planned. How could it have been? I didn't know that there would be a storm, let alone that we—that we...' She broke off, her face flaming as she heard him laugh harshly.

'That we would make love? You seem to find it difficult to say, yet you didn't appear to find it so difficult to do, and that surprised me, Helen, once I realised you were a virgin. Yet last night you lay in my arms and made love with me without a qualm and I have been asking myself why ever since. Was it because you were overcome with desire for me?' He shrugged, his fingers biting into her flesh as she tried to free herself. 'Possibly, but I imagine that came as rather a shock, something you hadn't planned on. I imagine what you really intended was to hit back at me, and what greater blow to a man's ego could there be than for the woman he has spent the night making love to to walk off without a word of farewell—just a note claiming that it had all been a mistake.'

Helen's head was reeling from the accusation but somehow she knew she had to convince Jacob he was wrong. It seemed imperative she do that! 'No! It wasn't like that. I didn't plan it, Jacob.' She struggled to find the courage to go on and make an admission which would leave her so very vulnerable. 'I—I made love with you last night because I wanted to and not for any other reason.'

Jacob barely glanced at her pleading face as he let her go and picked up the bottle of whisky to pour some into a glass. 'Indeed? How flattering, if I could believe it.' He tossed the whisky back, then set the glass down with a gentleness which was far more scary than any show of anger might have been. 'Last night was something you had planned, the same as that contract we signed. Perhaps you couldn't pin it down to a certain day or time but whenever it happened you were prepared to use it to your advantage. I congratulate you, Helen, you have a shrewd head.'

'Jacob, I——'

He cut her off as though she hadn't spoken, his voice like ice. 'That contract was quite precise, wasn't it, darling? If *I* decide to end our marriage within the first six months, then all the conditions will be met. But did you really hope to push me into doing that?' He laughed softly, dangerously. 'Sorry, Helen, but this marriage of ours will end only if and when I decide it will!'

He strode past her, his very bearing one of arrogant contempt, but there was no way this side of heaven that Helen was letting him leave after saying that! She ran after him, her nails biting through the fabric of his pale blue sweatshirt, her eyes glittering with fury. 'How dare you, Jacob? How dare you accuse me of planning such a thing?'

'Easily.' He smiled coolly. 'You've never made any secret of why you married me, have you? You set out to pay me back for all those supposed wrongs I've done your family. So what better way than to take me for every penny you can get? But I'm afraid you've misjudged me, Helen.'

Jacob's eyes held hers in a look which would have scared her rigid if it hadn't been for the anger she felt. 'If I had intended to hit back at you, then tell me why I've spent the past three hours trying to contact you! I could have let Richard get on with his rotten plans and sat back and watched you suffer. Frankly, I'm sorry I didn't do that!'

Jacob's eyes narrowed. 'What are you talking about? What is Richard up to?'

'I don't know, and that's what frightens me!' Suddenly her anger drained away and she let her hand drop from his arm in a gesture of despair. 'I don't know what he's been up to.'

Jacob took her by the arm and steered her back to a chair, making her sit down. 'Tell me what he said, every word.'

Helen's hand trembled as she ran it over her face. That Jacob should imagine her capable of that—but was it any wonder when they had spent these years inflicting wounds upon each other?

'Tell me, Helen.'

Jacob's voice was softer but it held a note which told her that he still believed what he'd accused her of. But for now she had to forget that and concentrate on what Richard had done. She couldn't bear the thought of Jacob suffering any more because of her. 'Richard arrived not long after I got back here. He'd seen me at the airport and followed me when he realised I was by myself.' She saw Jacob stiffen and understood at once the reason for it. 'Nothing happened, Jacob. Richard—well, he said a lot of things I don't need to repeat, but the gist of it was that he had decided to get even for being made to look a fool.'

Jacob swore colourfully, his face grim. 'So what did he tell you he had planned?'

Helen shook her head, the heavy red hair swinging around her shoulders. 'He didn't. He just said that by the time he was through you'd have nothing left. He seemed so sure of himself, Jacob!'

He smiled grimly. 'Did he indeed? Then I shall have to find out what he's been up to.' He glanced down at her, his eyes watchful. 'I wonder why you decided to warn me, though.'

She looked away from the searching gaze, her heart shuddering wildly. Jacob had been full of anger when he'd come after her tonight, yet it wasn't anger which seemed to flow between them now but something else, something which scared her even more. When Jacob drew her to her feet she kept her face averted, but he made her look at him.

'Do you still hate me, Helen?' His voice stroked every taut nerve, making her body hum with sensation. When her shocked eyes met his, all her uncertainties showed clearly in their cloudy emerald depths.

'No. I—I don't hate you.'

There was a moment when Jacob seemed to be turned to stone as his eyes held hers, then he bent and kissed her hard with a kind of savage triumph, his lips branding her with his mark. When he drew back just as abruptly and started towards the door, Helen took a step after him then stopped as he looked back, held there by the burning glitter in his eyes, the note in his deep voice.

'I've waited a long time for this, Helen. A very long time indeed!'

He was gone before she could stop him, before she could find her voice to ask him what he had meant, gone before the last fragile barrier crumbled and the truth filled her heart and mind. She loved Jacob. Deep down she had known how she felt for years, known that there would never be any other man for her, but she'd been afraid to admit it to herself, let alone to him. But soon, very soon, she would tell him the truth: that it wasn't hatred she felt, but love! She owed it to both of them to do that.

CHAPTER ELEVEN

ALMOST a week passed and Helen had no word from
Jacob. Each morning she awoke wondering if he would
contact her and each night went to bed disappointed.
She knew he was staying up in town from what her father
told her when she phoned him. Helen had glossed over
their unexpected return by using the storm as an excuse,
and Edward Sinclair had happily accepted the explanation. It was obvious that the stay in the country under
Baxter's attentive care had done him good. When he
offered to return to London so that the house would be
free, Helen refused. Until she had seen Jacob she intended to remain in town.

On Friday, after a near sleepless night spent worrying
about what was going on, Helen decided she could stand
it no longer. It was odd that Jacob hadn't even telephoned her but perhaps he had been too busy sorting
out whatever Richard had done. However, there was no
earthly reason why she shouldn't go to see him. She loved
him, and the need to tell him that at last was driving her
crazy.

Dressed in an attractive deep blue dress with her hair
swept into an elegant coil, she put the finishing touches
to her make-up, frowning at the shadows under her eyes.
She wanted to look her best when she saw Jacob, watch
his eyes fill with admiration and desire. She closed her
eyes as she recalled that last possessive kiss he had given
her, the note in his deep voice as he'd told her he had

waited a long time. What had he really meant? That he'd waited to hear her admit she didn't hate him? Or had there been something more to that statement? Had Jacob realised that she loved him because he felt the same way about her?

She savoured the thought, then roused herself when the letter-box rattled as a letter dropped on to the mat. Walking through to the hall, she picked it up and slit the envelope open, her attention more on what might happen when she saw Jacob, so that it took several seconds for the typewritten words to sink in. When they did the blood drained from her face.

It was from Jacob's solicitors, informing her that he was to start divorce proceedings and that they would be in touch with her own solicitors shortly. There had been no attempt to soften the stark words, probably because they imagined she knew what was to happen. Now the shock of it made her shake.

Jacob wanted a divorce! She couldn't bear even to think about it, not now when she finally knew how much she loved him. It must be some sort of silly mistake. When he had left the other night, divorce had been the last thing on his mind!

Later, Helen remembered nothing of the journey to Jacob's office. It was all a blank right up to the moment when she stood in front of his secretary's desk and demanded to know if he was in. Annette seemed to be torn between a desire to carry out her instructions and shock at the sight of Helen's white face. 'I'm afraid that Mr Hunt is busy at present, Miss Sinc—I mean, Mrs Hunt,' she amended hurriedly. 'He did say that he wasn't to be disturbed.'

'Did he?' Helen's eyes blazed as she glanced at the closed door to Jacob's office. 'I'm sure he will spare time to see me.'

Without another word she marched across the room and flung the door open, fighting to hold on to her control. It was all some sort of a mistake, that was all. Once she had spoken to Jacob then they would soon work it out.

Jacob was sitting behind his desk. He had his jacket off and his shirt sleeves rolled up, and there were dark shadows under his eyes which told their own story, but to Helen he looked simply marvellous. She drank in the sight of him, feeling her love warm away the cold fear. Then Jacob looked up, his gaze so impersonal that it swamped her afresh.

'Didn't Annette tell you I was busy, Helen?'

'I—yes, but I need to speak to you.'

He glanced at his watch then tipped back in his chair, watching her with hooded eyes. 'Then I can spare you a few minutes, I suppose. Make it brief.'

Helen closed the door and walked slowly across the room to stop in front of the desk. 'Why haven't you contacted me, Jacob?' she asked quietly.

He arched a brow, his handsome face full of mockery. 'So that's why you've come?' He sighed heavily. 'I've just told you, I've been busy.'

'Too busy to pick up the phone? I've been worried sick about what's been happening, whether you've sorted out what Richard was up to!' Her voice rose, reflecting her unease. Why was Jacob looking at her like that, his face full of that cool amusement? It wasn't how he had looked at her the other night. Then his eyes had been full of a fire just the memory of which could make her burn.

Suddenly she realised that he was speaking. 'I'm sorry. What did you say?'

He ran an impatient hand through his hair. 'I said that there is no need for you to worry about Richard's doings. That's all under control. Now, if that is the only reason why you came...' He picked up his pen, his meaning obvious, and Helen felt her temper rise. She stepped closer to the desk and opened her bag to take out the letter and thrust it towards him.

'It wasn't the only reason. I received this today. What exactly does it mean?'

Jacob barely spared it a glance, boredom etched on his face and in the eyes which lifted to hers. 'I imagine it's self-explanatory. I intend to divorce you.' He gave a soft little laugh which made her heart thump. 'Worried where that leaves you, Helen? Don't be. You will be well provided for under the terms of our contract. I doubt many women could fare so well. A few days of marriage and one night in bed in return for financial security for the rest of your life? Not bad, I'd say.'

'How dare you?' She didn't stop to think what she was doing as she struck out at his arrogant, mocking face, but he caught her wrist before her hand could make contact. Pushing it aside, he got up and came around the desk towards her, and despite her anger Helen shrank away from what she could see in his eyes, that bitter, icy disdain.

'I dare because I have waited a long time to achieve this. Did you imagine that you were the only one who wanted to settle old scores?' He caught her by the shoulders when she would have turned away, his fingers

biting into her flesh. 'Why did you come, Helen? Just
to ask about the letter? Or did you want to tell me how
you feel, that you love me?' His voice had dropped a
note but it held no warmth, just a dark ice which chilled
her. 'That's the truth, isn't it? You love me. I've always
known it even though you have claimed to hate me.' He
lifted her chin, forcing her to meet the icy amusement
in his eyes. 'Why do you really imagine that I married
you, Helen? Because I felt the same way? Because I
longed for you, wanted nothing more from life than to
have you as my wife and know that you loved me with
the same kind of obsessive madness?'

'Jacob, I...'

She couldn't carry on, the anguish tearing her apart
as she looked into his face and saw things which were
part of her worse nightmares. Yet even then he was relentless in his cruelty, driving it home.

'You what, Helen? Don't understand? Don't believe
me?' He shrugged, suddenly pushing her away as though
he found the idea of holding her distasteful. 'I married
you to get even, Helen. For all the things you and your
family did to me. And what better way to achieve that
objective than finally to make you admit that you were
in love with me? Now I imagine that even you understand that there is nothing more to add, apart from the
fact that my solicitor will be in touch with yours to
finalise all the arrangements.'

He went and sat down behind the desk again, picking
up his pen and turning his attention back to the papers
he was working on. Helen stared at him for one long
minute more, then turned and left, wondering how it
was possible to keep functioning when it felt as though
her heart had just been ripped to shreds. On leaden legs

she left the office block and made her way back to the flat, then instead of going inside went to her car and climbed behind the wheel and just sat there, staring along the drive. It had all been a trick, a cruel, deliberate, perfectly planned trick! Jacob must have hated her for years and realised that he had it within his power to make her pay for all her foolishness, all the hurts she and her family had inflicted on him. He had helped her father when Edward had asked him, not for any altruistic reason but because it had been a means to tighten the net and achieve what he wanted: to make her admit she loved him so that he could throw that love back in her face. She didn't think that she could bear it.

It took less than an hour to drive to the house but it felt as though a hundred years had passed since she'd woken up that morning. She had longed to tell Jacob that she loved him, but now she knew what a farce that really was. Jacob hated her and the realisation almost tore her apart.

She pulled into the driveway and sat for a few minutes to compose herself before getting out and ringing the bell. It wasn't going to be easy to explain to her father what a mistake she'd made, but it had to be done. No matter what Jacob had said, she wouldn't accept a penny of his money either for herself or for her father. Every penny would be tainted by the hatred he felt for her.

Edward Sinclair was in the library reading one of the old-fashioned fishing handbooks he was so fond of. Baxter showed her in then discreetly left, although Helen wasn't unaware of the man's surprise at her unexpected appearance, the stilted tone of her voice. She was holding on by just a thread and it showed.

'Helen! Darling, what a lovely surprise. You should have phoned and come down earlier for lunch.' Edward Sinclair put his book down and got up to greet her. He wasn't using his stick, Helen noticed. Obviously the rest and care had done him good and she hated the thought that she was about to bring him fresh worries, but it couldn't be helped. Jacob hated her!

The thought brought tears to her eyes so unexpectedly that she had no time to prevent her father from seeing them, and turned away when she heard his murmur of dismay.

'Darling, what is it? Has something happened?' He came and put his arm around her, holding her close as he had done so many times when she'd been a child and cried about some small injury or injustice. She'd believed then that her father could cure all ills, but he couldn't cure what ailed her now, this pain which was tearing her apart. And the thought made her cry all the harder until her body was racked with sobs.

When her father led her to the comfortable old chesterfield and made her sit down, she went obediently, pouring out the whole story at his gentle probing. He waited until she had finished then got up and walked slowly to the window, his back towards her as he stared across the lawns.

'And you really believe that Jacob married you to pay you back? That it was merely some sort of act of revenge?'

'Yes—he made it clear.' Tears welled into her eyes again and she wiped them away with her fingers.

'Well, there's none so blind as those who won't see.' Her father sighed as he turned round, and smiled at her puzzled expression. 'Helen, you can't see what is staring you in the face. You never have been able to see it.'

'Father, I don't——'

'Don't understand?' He came back and sat down next to her, taking her hand as he smiled gently at her. 'Jacob has been in love with you for years, darling. Everyone knew that. Why do you think your mother went to such lengths to keep him away from you, telling Baxter that he wasn't to pass on any messages, inform you of any telephone calls? Your mother and I both knew that he was besotted with you and—well, I'm afraid we both felt that he wasn't good enough for you.'

'Father!'

'Oh, I know, I know. I'm not proud of it now, not when I see what a fine man Jacob has turned into, but back then there was a wildness about him which worried both your mother and me. Perhaps we were just afraid because you were so young and Jacob Hunt was something beyond your experience. But he was in love with you then, the same as he is still in love with you to this very day.'

'I—no! You're wrong. He doesn't love me—he hates me!'

'Helen, it's you who are wrong. In a way it's my fault because I should have told you that Jacob wasn't the one who destroyed our business and took this house and everything away from us. I did that through my own incompetence. Jacob merely tried to help afterwards.'

'He told me that you had asked him to?' Helen could barely speak, the shock of what her father had just said stealing the words.

'It was the truth. I went to him and asked him to help bail out the company and myself. And do you know why it was Jacob I went to, darling?'

'Because he was in a position to help?' she suggested hesitantly.

Edward smiled. 'Jacob is a businessman. Taking on an ailing company and all its debts made little sense, but I knew he was my only hope because I knew how he felt about you, darling. Shameful, wasn't it? I played on his feelings for you to save us from bankruptcy.'

Helen's head was reeling with shock. Her father sounded as though he believed it, but he could be wrong. Love could die; Jacob's love for her could have changed to hatred. 'It doesn't explain why he told me the exact opposite before. He—he's instructed his solicitors to start divorce proceedings.'

'Has he? Then if I were you, Helen, I would start to ask myself why.' He shook his head when she started to speak. 'Jacob loves you. I have no doubts about that. If he has told you differently then he must have had a reason, one that might not be immediately obvious.' He looked quietly into her eyes. 'Do you love him, Helen? Really love him?'

She closed her eyes on a sudden wave of pain. 'Yes!'

'Then don't let him lie to you about this. I don't know why he's doing it, but if you love him then don't let it end without putting up a fight.'

Helen stared at her father in silence as a thought started to grow, an idea which filled her with both fear and hope. Had Jacob been so cruel because of Richard and what he had done? Richard had told her that he intended to see that Jacob lost everything, so how successful had he been in that aim? If Jacob lost everything he owned he

would hate it, would hate the idea that he couldn't give
Helen what he thought she wanted to keep her happy.
How wrong he was! All she needed in her life was Jacob.
Nothing else mattered.

Staff were streaming out of the doors when Helen arrived at the towering block where Jacob had his office.
Edward Sinclair had insisted that his daughter wait until
she had composed herself before setting off on the drive
back to town and, although Helen had been torn by im-
patience, she knew that it made sense. Now as she stood
on the pavement outside the fast-emptying building she
said a silent prayer that she hadn't made the journey in
vain.

No one stopped her as she made her way up in the
lift to Jacob's office. Everyone was too intent on getting
home after a long day. When she reached the floor which
housed Hunt Electronics it was deserted, as was the outer
office Annette usually guarded.

Helen's heart sank. Somehow she'd never given any
thought to the fact that Jacob might not be there. The
need to speak to him and find out if her father had been
right was burning inside her, a flame which threatened
to consume her. She *had* to know one way or the other
if there was any room for hope.

Later she had no idea what kept her hesitating in the
silent office. Perhaps it was just a reluctance to leave
without doing anything at all. Yet as she stood there she
was suddenly filled with a growing certainty that Jacob
was still in the building. She could sense his presence
like an almost physical thing. Slowly she walked across
to the door of his room and turned the handle, pushing

the door wide open so that she could see inside the room, and felt her heart contract at what she saw.

Jacob was sitting slumped in one of the soft leather chairs beside the window, his eyes closed, his whole bearing one of utter dejection. Helen had never seen him like this before in her life, never seen the vitality drained out of him before. Jacob was always in control, brimming with energy and confidence, master of his destiny, yet the man seated in the chair looked far removed from that description.

'Are you all right, Jacob?' Her voice was soft as she asked the question yet he jerked upright as though he had been struck. Just for a moment he met her worried gaze, his eyes unguarded, then the mask dropped back into place to hide his feelings from her.

'What do you want, Helen?' His tone was little short of rude, so brusque that a few minutes before Helen would have turned and run, but not now, not after what she had witnessed so fleetingly in his eyes just now!

Just the memory of what she had seen gave her courage, stemmed the tremble which coursed through her limbs, made her voice ring out firm and clear. 'To speak to you, of course.'

He stood up abruptly, pushing his dishevelled hair back from his forehead with a hand which trembled slightly despite the rigid control Helen guessed he was keeping on his emotions. 'I think we said all that needed to be said before. Anything else can be dealt with through our solicitors.'

Helen arched an amused brow, moving across the room to stop beside him, so close that her arm brushed his, and she felt the way he flinched at the slight contact with a feeling of joy. 'Can it really? So what do you suggest, Jacob? That I instruct my solicitor to write informing you that I am head over heels in love with you and that I have no intention of allowing you to divorce me for all the misguided reasons you've decided on?'

'Helen, I . . .'

'What?' She laid her hand on his arm, feeling the way the muscles under the thin shirt contracted immediately. 'You are going to tell me that you don't care, that making me admit I love you was all part of your plan?' She laughed softly, seductively, as she smoothed her hand up his arm and down again. 'What a monstrous lie, Jacob Hunt. You love me just as much as I love you. You always have. *That* is the reason why you wanted to marry me. So let's see if you're man enough to admit it?'

His whole body went rigid, his face taut with an emotion which someone else might have mistaken for anger, but not Helen. Her father had been right, she'd been blind to all the signs but now she was going to look at Jacob and see—really see for the first time in her life!

'I don't know where you got that ridiculous idea from, Helen. But I suggest that you disabuse yourself of it very quickly. Now I cannot see that we have anything left to discuss so if you'll excuse me——'

'You're very busy? Is that what you are about to say, Jacob, darling?' She stepped in front of him when he tried to move past her, one hand lifting to press gently against his chest. Under her palm she felt his heart jerk then start to beat crazily, and she smiled as she moved her fingers over the betraying signal he couldn't hide.

'That's enough! I don't know what's got into you, Helen.'

Jacob's eyes were burning as they met hers, his fingers bruising as they grasped her wrist and dragged her hand away from him, but Helen wasn't deterred. She loved him and he loved her and she would be damned if she would let him ruin what they could have by lying out of some stupid sense of duty!

'Love, Jacob. That's what's got into me. It's taken me a long time to realise it, but there's no way I'm going to let you try to ruin something marvellous.'

He pushed her away, his movements jerky and un-coordinated as he walked across the room to the window and stood there with his back towards her. 'You're making a fool of yourself, Helen,' he said harshly.

Her heart turned over at the cold assertion, but from somewhere she found strength to carry on. 'If anyone is being a fool it's you, darling. You love me. You know you do. I don't understand completely but I think your determination to push me out of your life has something to do with Richard and what he's done.'

She walked over to the window and stopped just behind him. In the night-darkened glass she could see both their reflections, two separate people until she moved another slow step closer to him and they merged into one. And suddenly she knew without the slightest doubt that this had been meant. She and Jacob were two halves which made one whole, two shadows which merged, two souls which joined until eternity.

'I love you, Jacob. I wouldn't care if you were penniless. It won't change how I feel. I love you.'

He swung round, his face set into harsh lines. 'Won't it?' He laughed bitterly. 'Believe me, you have no idea, Helen. That sort of strain can kill any feelings dead very quickly despite all your pretty words. Ironic, isn't it, that

I've spent the past few years fighting to get to the top just so that I would have something to offer you, and now this comes along?'

He turned away to walk to the desk and open a drawer. He pulled out a thick folded document and laid it on top of the desk. 'But no matter what happens, Helen, you will be provided for. The house has already been signed over into your name along with the flat and enough shares to guarantee an income. That's all I can offer you now, so take it.'

Helen followed him across the room and picked up the document then calmly ripped it in half and tossed it back on to the desk. 'I don't want the house or the flat or shares. I want you, Jacob—just you, but if you are too damned pig-headed to accept that then there's nothing I can do about it!'

She swung round on her heel and walked swiftly towards the door, her heart thumping painfully. Please stop me, she prayed silently. Please, please, see what you are doing, Jacob! Yet she reached the door and still Jacob didn't say a word. Helen grasped the handle, then felt her whole body jerk with reaction when behind her Jacob said suddenly, 'Don't go!'

Her heart was hammering so hard that she thought she would faint, but somehow she hung on as she turned to look at him. 'Why, Jacob? Why don't you want me to leave?'

'Because I love you, Helen!' The words seemed to be torn from him, his voice hoarse with strain. 'So help me, I love you and even knowing that I should let you go isn't enough!'

'It is, darling. Love is more than enough. It's everything we need.'

'Is it?' He came over to her then, taking her hands to hold them tightly, his eyes burning with an almost feverish need. 'It could get tough, Helen. You must understand that. I can cope with the thought of that but I can't cope with the thought of losing you again because of it. I've waited half my life for you, my love. I don't think I could stand to have you taken from me again.'

Tears stung Helen's eyes as she reached up to brush his cheek with a kiss of infinite tenderness, loving him more than she'd thought possible. 'That won't happen, Jacob. I love you. I always have. I think deep down I knew it and that's what scared me, why I always ran from you. But no matter what happens it won't change my feelings for you. Has Richard done much damage?'

Jacob drew her into his arms and held her as though he would never let her go again as he brushed fleetingly tormenting kisses over her face. 'Basically, no. If it had happened at any other time then its effects would have been minimal, but I've been putting together a rather large deal recently which has stretched the company's assets to the limit. It appears that Richard has been liaising with an American firm which is one of our biggest rivals. They have been trying to get their hands on shares in Hunt Electronics to make a takeover bid and Richard has been putting them in touch with possible vendors.'

Helen gasped. 'That's awful! How could he do such a thing?'

Jacob smoothed his hand down her cheek before bending to kiss her lingeringly. 'Because he was jealous of my marrying you, sweet. I don't applaud his methods, but I can understand them.'

'But what will you do? Can you stop them?'

'I aim to try. They're offering a lot of money for the shares and I know it's going to be a big temptation to a number of shareholders. If I could meet the price and offer to buy them myself then there would be no problem, but right now that's impossible. There is a chance that I will be able to get backing from one of the big banks, but if anything goes wrong then I could lose the lot.'

'But it won't, Jacob.' She laughed softly. 'I called you tough and ruthless once and that's what you are, only this time I do mean it as a compliment. If anyone can pull the company through then it's you, Jacob! And I wouldn't be at all surprised to discover that fewer of those shareholders than you imagine will be willing to sell. They know who they can rely on, Jacob, and you won't let them down!'

Jacob smiled suddenly, holding her so close that she could feel the heavy thud of his heartbeat joining with hers. 'I'll do my damnedest, Helen. With you standing beside me then, yes, I think it will be all right.'

'Of course it will. We've waited too long for this to let it go now just because of your stubborn male pride!'

'Insults shouldn't go unpunished, Helen.'

Her eyes loved him. 'Mmm, I can hardly wait. But you deserve me calling you a few names. I love you, I need you. Just you, Jacob—nothing else.'

He twined his fingers through her hair, pulling out the pins so that it fell in glorious waves around her shoulders. 'I'm crazy about you, Helen. I have been since the first time I laid eyes on you all those years ago. I saw you and fell in love, it was as simple as that. I think I must be the luckiest man alive because finally every dream I've had has come true.'

'For me too.' She gave a tremulous smile, the depth of Jacob's feelings for her overwhelming her. She didn't deserve to be loved like this, but she would spend her life making sure that he never regretted it. When he bent and kissed her she responded eagerly, her lips clinging to his as she let him know how she felt, let him understand that all the waiting hadn't been in vain. Jacob was the only man she would ever want, and she told him that as he moved his mouth to her neck to trail disturbingly sensuous kisses along it.

He framed her face in his hands, his eyes burning into hers. 'If I don't get you somewhere where I can make love to you soon, Helen, I'll go crazy!'

She nibbled his mouth, drawing away when he started to respond. Glancing over her shoulder she cast a pointed look at the soft leather sofa, then disentangled herself from his arms. With a slow deliberation she unbuttoned her jacket and tossed it carelessly aside, then looked back at him, one brow arching as her hands went to the long zip at the back of her dress before she started to inch it down, loving the faint groan Jacob gave. When she had pulled the zip all the way down, she kicked off her shoes then stopped, a faintly questioning look on her face.

'Last time I did this, Jacob, you stopped me.'

He gave a short, hoarse laugh, reaching for her to pull her hard against him, intent written clearly on his face and in the depths of his eyes. 'That was a mistake I have no intention of repeating!'

Helen smiled as his mouth claimed hers, her eyes closing on a wave of joy. They had made mistakes, both of them, but they were all in the past. Now they had the future to look forward to, a future filled with love—and love could never be a mistake.

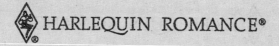

HARLEQUIN ROMANCE®

brings you

More Romances Celebrating Love, Families and Children!

Harlequin Romance #3362

THE BABY BUSINESS

by

Rebecca Winters

If you love babies—this book is for you!

When hotel nanny Rachel Ellis searches for her lost brother, she meets his boss—the dashing and gorgeous Vincente de Raino. She is unprepared for her strong attraction to him, but even more unprepared to be left holding the baby—his adorable baby niece, Luisa, who makes her long for a baby of her own!

Available in May wherever Harlequin Books are sold.

KIDS12

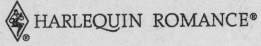 **HARLEQUIN ROMANCE®**

brings you

Harlequin Romance #3361, *Mail-Order Bridegroom*,
in our Sealed with a Kiss series next month is by one of
our most popular authors, **Day Leclaire**.

Leah Hampton needs a husband for her ranch
to survive—a strictly no-nonsense business arrangement.
Advertising for one in the local newspaper makes good
sense, but she finds to her horror a reply from none other
than Hunter Pryde, the man she had been in love with
eight years before!

Is her fate sealed with one kiss? Or can she resist falling
in love with him all over again?

In the coming months, look for these exciting
Sealed with a Kiss stories:

Harlequin Romance #3366
P.S. I Love You by Valerie Parv in June

Harlequin Romance #3369
Wanted: Wife and Mother by Barbara McMahon in July